ON-TRACK
ON BRITISH RAILWAYS

(Formerly "Track Machines")

by

Roger Butcher

FOURTH EDITION

Published by Platform 5 Publishing Ltd., Lydgate House, Lydgate Lane, Sheffield S10 5FH, England.

Printed by Icon Impressions, Yorkshire Street Mills, Yorkshire Street, Bacup, Lancashire OL13 9AF.

ISBN 1 872524 22 2

Speno RPS32-1 train DR 79215–20 is seen approaching Leicester on 15th February 1990.

Ian R. Attenborough

CONTENTS

ACKNOWLEDGEMENTS

I would like to record my thanks to Cowans Boyd, Geismar, Matisa, Permaquip, Plasser, Speno, Tamper and Wickham Rail for the photographs and information they have very kindly provided. Particular thanks are due to the staff of Plasser Railway Machinery (GB) Ltd. who have always been very tolerant of my interest in their machines. I would specifically like to acknowledge the help of the now retired Works Manager Mr Leo Pilgerstorfer, the Works and Technical Manager Mr Herbert Pilgerstorfer, Mr Hans Mueller, Steve, Stan and Alfred. I would also like to sincerely thank the many railway staff from all points of BR, who have for many years been regularly assisting me in my efforts to maintain an accurate and comprehensive register of BR On-track plant.

Thanks also to all the companies, particularly Balfour Beatty Railway Engineering, for all the assistance given to me whilst compiling the section on contractors' track machines. Thanks as always to Keith, Roger, Roy and the KBTCB for their help on various aspects of this book. Finally, a grateful thank-you to Diane and Mark whose continuing support and encouragement has been greatly appreciated.

Roger Butcher, March 1991

INTRODUCTION

Although the first three editions of this book bore the title 'Track Machines' it was often suggested that 'BR Special Plant' or 'BR On-Track Plant' would perhaps be more appropriate. In view of the requests of the four major suppliers in Britain of on-track plant to advertise in this new edition and the expansion of the book to include contractors, industrial and other railways track machines the new title 'On-Track Plant on British Railways' was chosen.

A range of new machines have been purchased whilst in addition there has been a significant number of disposals and changes in allocations and this fourth edition reflects the very latest situation. There have of course been many excellent technical articles in the various railway engineering journals and elsewhere and it should again be stated clearly it is in that direction that readers requiring detailed technical information should look. The principle aim of this book is simply to detail accurately what on-track plant British Railways possesses, to give where appropriate some basic details and descriptions and to state where it is allocated.

The following notes on the numbering systems utilised will give a good indication of what there is to be seen. Until 1967, RCE Plant was purchased regionally and consequently there was a multiplicity of numbering schemes. In 1957 the Eastern Region began using the DB 965XXX number series, this series being described as "Service vehicles other than C & W types". Some uniformity was established in 1958 when the Scottish and Southern Regions began using the same series. From 1967 when a central purchasing policy for major plant was introduced, the DB 965XXX series now included London Midland and Western vehicles. London Midland vehicles purchased prior to 1967 were 'numbered up' in the DB 9654XX and DB 9655XX series, but pre-1967 Western Region machines still retained their old PWM numbers. The Western Region continued to use PWM numbers for their track-machines until 1974 and in the 1967–74 period some machines were allocated both PWM numbers and DB 965XXX numbers, whilst others only received PWM numbers.

1974 saw the introduction of Civil Engineers Plant System (CEPS) numbers. This new system was basically a variation of the Eastern Region's own on-track plant number scheme. It is similar to that used for locomotives in that the first two digits indicate the type of machine and the third digit its sub-type. From 1974 to 1977 new machines ordered were allocated numbers in both this series and the DB 96XXXX series. The final allocation to the latter series was DB 966095 (Matisa B 341 4970028 1978), whilst DB 969000–79 were also allocated in 1977 as the DB 967XXX and DB 968XXX series were already in use. Seven years later in 1984 the numbers ADB 965576–81 were issued to cover the conversion of six new snowploughs, whilst in 1989 the numbers ADB 966096–9 were used for the conversion of a further four snowploughs. Snowploughs of course do not come under the CEPS scheme.

Machines ordered from 1978 were allocated only CEPS numbers and regions were specifically asked not to allocate their own regional identifications. Various modifications to this system have taken place since its commencement and the current system can be summarised as follows:

DR   Reportable to TOPS
DX   Not reportable to TOPS

For Twin Jib Cranes (commonly known as Track Relayers or TRMs) and cranes – these being reportable to TOPS – a suffix letter is added to indicate builders.

A	Booth
B	BR
C	Cowans Sheldon/Clarke Chapman/Cowans Boyd
F	Coles
G	Grafton
H	Hap Cranes
J	Jones
M	Marshall Fleming
P	Plasser and Theurer
R	Ransome and Rapier
S	Smith
T	Taylor and Hubbard
V	Cravens
W	Warwell/Atlas

For those not owned by the RCE a prefix letter is added to indicate owning department:

A	Mechanical & Electrical Engineer
K	Signal & Telecommunications Engineer

L	M&EE Electrical Construction
T	Operating Department

The main number ranges are continually being extended and can be summarised as follows:

		Sub-Types
68XXX	Personnel Carriers	0/8/9
69XXX	RCE Wagon–mounted Snowblowers	0
72XXX	Ballast Consolidators/Track Stabilisers	0/1/2
73XXX	Tamper/Liners	0/1/2/3/4/5/6/7/8/9
74XXX	Tampers (original use)	0/1/2/3/4/5/6
75XXX	Mid-Range Tamper/Liners	0/1/2
75XXX	Liners (original use)	0/1/2
76XXX	Ballast Cleaners	0/1/2/3/4/5
77XXX	Ballast Regulators	0/1/2/3/4/5/6/7
78XXX	Track Relayers	0/1/2/3/4/5
79XXX	Miscellaneous	0/1/2/3/4/5
80XXX	RCE Steam Cranes	0/1
81XXX	RCE Diesel Cranes	0/1/2/3/4/5
82XXX	Viaduct Inspection Units	0/1/2/3
85XXX	Trenching Units	0
86XXX	Rail Joint Straighteners	0/1/2
88XXX	Skip Train	1/2/3
89XXX	CWR Trains	0/1/2
90XXX	Track Recorders (ex-50XXX)	0
94XXX	Sleeper Squarers	4/5/6
95XXX	M & EE Steam Cranes	0/1/2
96XXX	M & EE Diesel Cranes	0/1/2/3/4/5/7/8
97XXX	Departmental Locomotives	6
98XXX	General Purpose Maintenance Vehicles	1/2/3/4/5/6/7/8

All track machines fitted with buffers and drawgear and compatible brake systems are having their prefixes altered to DR in order that they may be reportable to TOPS. Some machines however have still yet to receive their correct prefixes and in the interests of simplicity this book details the prefix that should, and will in due course, be carried. Also mention should be made that as it is the intention that all TRAMMs should eventually be reportable to TOPS, new build 98213–21 have been prefixed DR. There are no immediate plans to change the prefixes of those TRAMMs already in service.

The book has been divided into seven separate sections and unless stated otherwise the layout of each section is such that the first column is the CEPS number, the second column is the DB 96XXXX number (where applicable), the third column indicates any regional identity, whilst the fourth and fifth columns show builders number and year of building respectively. In common with the practice of the Industrial Railway Society this book quotes the date appearing on the works plate. If there is no date on the works plate or indeed no works plate, the date quoted will be that when the machine was delivered new to BR.

The final column gives the area (or regional if appropriate) allocation, or its specific location if stored out of use (OOU). In the case of engineers trolleys, personnel carriers and the smaller general purpose maintenance vehicles the base location is given. A list of the depots where machines are maintained is included on page 96.

Mention should also be made that as from the spring of 1991 the first phase of replacing regions by profit centres is due to commence. This reorganisation is planned to be completed by 1993 and the next edition of this book will fully reflect the changes in machine allocations that will have taken place.

The sections on trolleys, track-machines, track-relayers and cranes are split into two parts, the first part detailing current stock as at February 1991 whilst the second part gives a brief history of vehicles no longer in existence but which had CEPS numbers. This therefore gives a complete record of those machines allocated CEPS numbers. In addition details of machines due to enter service during 1991 are included.

ERRATUM

Please note that the captions of the two photographs on page 90 are reversed. We apologise for this error.

Permaquip Patrolman's vehicle DX 68811 is pictured at Perth on 27th August 1988.   Permaquip

In 1985/6 Permaquip supplied twelve powered canopy trolleys to British Rail, their original CEPS numbers being DX 68700–11. Although officially renumbered DX 98700–11, many still carry their original numbers including DX 98703 pictured here at Northampton CMD on 25th January 1989.

Colin Underhill

TROLLEYS AND GENERAL PURPOSE MAINTENANCE VEHICLES

68XXX PERSONNEL CARRIERS

This group of plant numbers was originally described as either Engineers Trolleys or Track Inspection Trolleys, but following the introduction in 1985 of no less than five new types of vehicles, it was decided that the description General Purpose Maintenance Vehicles would be more appropriate.

In 1987 a regrouping of vehicle types occurred and only those vehicles for which regular individual maintenance costs are not required remain in this numbering series. Consequently this series now only covers the largely life-expired DX 680XX fleet and the more recent DX 688XX and DX 689XX personnel carriers. Those vehicles for which regular individual maintenance costs are required have been renumbered into the DX 98XXX series and that number series now includes the former DX 681XX, DX 682XX, DX 683XX, DX 685XX, DX 686XX and DX 687XX types of vehicles, the first digit of each vehicle being changed from a 6 to a 9.

The DX 680XX series are almost all Wickham engineers' trolleys and trailers, although DX 68025–31 are conversions from Matisa Consolidators, whilst DX 68035/6/97 are tug units built by Permaquip. DX 68038/43 are Wickham trolleys rebuilt at Doncaster Marshgate for use as tunnel inspection trolleys. DX 68043–7 are not officially allocated CEPS numbers, but are included in order to provide a complete list of current trolleys and converted trailers.

Also included here for convenience is the Permaquip Materials Handling Tug purchased by the S&T in 1989. As it is not a Civil Engineers' machine, it does not of course have a CEPS number.

The Wickham range of engineers trolleys are powered personnel carriers for use by engineering staff, the more modern ones having sheet metal ends and roofs and roll-up canvas sides which when let down and secured enclose the vehicle from the elements. They have a glass windscreen and can travel forwards and backwards and have seats for about twelve staff. Maximum permitted speed is 25 mph on plain line, 15 mph over switch and crossings and 5 mph when a trailer is being propelled.

Despite predictions to the contrary a significant number of Wickham engineers' trolleys are still at work in January 1991. Such is their popularity the Southern Region sent DX 68078 to Wickham Rail in July 1990 to establish the costs of a complete refurbishment and the replacement of canvas sides by enclosed metal sides.

Also included within the DX 680XX series are steel-framed trailers that work with trolleys. These can be categorised as follows:

(1) DX 68014/5/20/3/4/45–7/72/7/81/4/5/93 are conversions from trolleys (2 ton capacity)
(2) DX 68039–42/96 are purpose built (2 ton capacity)
(3) DX 68074/6/9/83/7/9/91/4/5 are purpose built (4 ton capacity)

The numbers 68032–4/43–9 were not officially issued.

DX 68800–10 are Permaquip Personnel Carriers, DX 68800–4 displacing the last surviving London Midland Region Wickham engineers trolleys. DX 68805–10 have been allocated to the Southern Region and Wickham trailers DX 68076/9/83/9/94/5 have been modified by Permaquip so that they can work with DX 68805–10. The Permaquip Personnel Carrier has a water cooled diesel engine and has a maximum speed of 40 mph. It is also fitted with integral floodlighting and can carry nine men. Also provided are full messing facilities, whilst the Personnel Carrier can be on and off tracked using the Permaquip Tracess system.

DX 68811 is known as a Patrolman's vehicle and is a track inspection saloon with a water cooled diesel engine and a maximum speed of 50 mph. Messing facilities and on and off-tracking facilities are also provided. DX 68812 is a Road/Rail Track Welding Vehicle adapted from Zweiweg KYH 862X, originally a Breakdown Unit. Also on the Scottish Region is DX 68813, a Road/Rail Unimog purchased second-hand and equipped with a small crane.

DX 68901–6 are Bruff Road/Rail Mercedes 307D Personnel Carriers. DX 68901–4 having been delivered late in 1987. DX 68901–3 were initially allocated to the Southern Region, whilst DX 68904 was delivered to the London Midland Region. However DX 68901/3/4 were transferred in 1989 to the Scottish Region whilst DX 68902 was due to be reallocated to the Western Region in January 1991. DX 68905 is the support vehicle for Road/Rail Viaduct Inspection Unit 82301, whilst DX 68906 performs the same function for Road/Rail Tunnel Inspection Unit 14201. These vehicles enable the easy transportation of up to nine staff with hand tools to the rail site. They can be turned on their own hydraulic turntable to enable on/off tracking, whilst also provided are full messing facilities.

DX 68907/8 are Mercedes 17-tonne lorries which have been transformed into multi-purpose road/rail vehicles by Permaquip fitting their Fairmont Hy-Rail equipment onto a standard commercial vehicle. DX 68907/8 are due to be in service in January 1991.

As regards allocation, the vehicle's base location is given but it should be emphasised that they will often be found elsewhere in that particular civil engineering area.

Engineers Trolleys and Trailers (Various Manufacturers)

Current Stock:

DX 68003(a)	DB 965951	68/007	10647 1972	Horsforth
DX 68004	–	PWM 2831	5009 1949	Exmouth Jn.
DX 68005	DB 965949	68/005	10645 1972	Stanningley
DX 68006	DB 965950	68/006	10646 1972	Newcastle Forth Bank
DX 68007	–	PWM 4303	7506 1956	Exmouth Jn.
DX 68008	DB 965952	68/008	10648 1972	Whitby
DX 68009	–	PWM 4305	7508 1956	Exmouth Jn.
DX 68010	DB 965987	68/010	10731 1974	Darlington Park Lane
DX 68011	DB 965045	DE 900856	7073 1955	Darlington Park Lane
DX 68013	DB 965071	DE 320489	7586 1957	Tees Yard
DX 68014(b)	DB 965073	DE 320491	7588 1957	Darlington Park Lane
DX 68015(b)	DB 965078	DE 320496	7593 1957	Whitby
DX 68016	DB 965079	DE 320497	7594 1957	Glaisdale
DX 68017	DB 965080	DE 320498	7595 1957	Darlington Park Lane
DX 68018	DB 965083	DE 320501	7598 1957	Darlington Park Lane OOU
DX 68020(b)	DB 965085	DE 320503	7600 1957	Whitby
DX 68022	DB 965096	DE 320514	7611 1957	Northallerton Low Gates
DX 68023(b)	DB 965099	DE 320517	7614 1957	Darlington Park Lane
DX 68024(b)	DB 965102	DE 320520	7617 1957	Northallerton Low Gates
DX 68030	DB 965369	70/008	D8005 1971	Slateford OOU
DX 68031	DB 965575	MCM 72/1	D8014 1972	Dundee Tay Bridge
DX 68035	–	–	FBT1 1982	Dalmeny
DX 68036	–	–	TB001 1982	Dalmeny
DX 68038	–	–	1947 1935	Doncaster Marshgate OOU
		rebuilt Doncaster Marshgate 1982		
DX 68039(b)	DB 965953	–	10649 1972	Whitby
DX 68042(b)	DB 965956	–	10652 1972	Marsden OOU
(DX 68043)	–	–	Wickham	Doncaster Marshgate
		rebuilt Doncaster Marshgate 1983		
(DX 68044)	DB 965097	DE 320515	7612 1957	Darlington Park Lane
(DX 68045)(b)	–	DE 900420	730 1932	Newcastle Forth Bank
(DX 68046)(b)	DB 965075	DE 320493	7590 1957	Ferryhill
(DX 68047)(b)	–	PWM 3960	6945 1955	Exmouth Jn.
DX 68071	DB 965336	–	10343 1969	Ashford Plant Depot OOU
DX 68073	DB 965990	–	10705 1974	Ashford Plant Depot OOU
DX 68074(b)	DB 965162	–	8384 1959	Canterbury East
DX 68075	DB 965991	–	10707 1974	Purley
DX 68076(b)	DB 966042	–	10850 1975	Purley
DX 68078	DB 965992	–	10708 1974	Ashford Plant Depot
DX 68079(b)	DB 966040	–	10848 1975	Ramsgate
DX 68080	DB 965993	–	10706 1974	Hastings
DX 68081(b)	–	DS 52	7031 1954	Hastings
DX 68082	DB 966031	–	10839 1975	Wimbledon Park
DX 68083(b)	DB 966038	–	10846 1975	Sevenoaks
DX 68084(b)	–	DS 3317	(7824 1957)?	Wimbledon Park
DX 68086	DB 966033	–	10841 1975	Canterbury East
DX 68087(b)	DB 965161	–	8385 1959	Folkestone East
DX 68088	DB 966034	–	10842 1975	Folkestone East
DX 68089(b)	DB 966037	–	10845 1975	Tonbridge East
DX 68090	DB 966035	–	10843 1975	Swanley OOU
DX 68091(b)	DB 965160	–	8386 1959	Swanley OOU
DX 68094(b)	DB 966041	–	10849 1975	Sole Street
DX 68095(b)	DB 966039	–	10847 1975	Hassocks
DX 68097	–	–	T003 1988	Aylesbury
–	(c)	–	T004 1989	Eastleigh

(a) Originally numbered DX 68007, but number altered to avoid a duplicate number. Unfortunately there was also another DX 68003!
(b) These are steel-framed trailers that work with trolleys. Details of which are purpose built and which are conversions from trolleys can be found in the introductory notes on this section.
(c) Owned by the S&T New Works Section.

Vehicles no longer in stock:

DX 68000   DB 965132   RMT 57/3   7844 1957
Type 40 Mk I Wickham trolley initially allocated to Inverness. Later Strathcarron, Crianlarich Upper and Spean Bridge. Scrapped at Kilmarnock RCE Workshops by Howard and Pepperell, Sheffield 1/81.

DX 68001   DB 965135   RMT 57/4   7847 1957
Type 40 Mk I Wickham trolley initially allocated to Inverness. Later Crianlarich Upper and Spean Bridge. Scrapped at Kilmarnock RCE Workshops by a private contractor 4/82.

DX 68002   DB 965330   RMT 68/1   10180 1968
Type 18A Mark X Wickham trolley. Mainly allocated to Crianlarich Upper. Sold from Kilmarnock RCE Workshops to the Ayrshire Railway Preservation Society, Dalmellington 3/80.

DX 68003   DB 965331   RMT 68/2   10179 1968
Type 18A Mark X Wickham trolley. Mainly allocated to Georgemas Jn. Later Spean Bridge and Glenfinnan. Sold from Spean Bridge to the Ayrshire Railway Preservation Society, Dalmellington 4/86.

DX 68012   DB 965065   DE 320483   7580 1956
Type 17A Wickham trolley initially delivered to Gateshead and allocated to Fencehouses. Later Haltwhistle from where it was sold to the Forest of Dean Railway 7/85.

DX 68018   DB 965082   DE 320500   7597 1957
Type 17A Wickham trolley initially delivered to York and allocated to Glaisdale. Later Grosmont and Battersby. Sold from Darlington ODM Depot to the South Tynedale Preservation Society, Alston 12/86.

DX 68021   DB 965092   DE 320510   7607 1957
Type 17A Wickham trolley initially delivered to Gateshead and allocated to Haltwhistle. Later Dunston Staithes. Finally Tyne Yard where it was damaged in a shunting accident. Scrapped at Tyne Yard by Seagrave, West Auckland 4/86.

DX 68025   DB 965392   CB 10   D8 006 1971
Matisa D8 Consolidator allocated to the Birmingham Division. Converted at Newton Heath RCE Works in 1980 to an inspection trolley and allocated to Welshpool. Transferred to CAD Longtown 1983. Scrapped at Carlisle Kingmoor Yard by Ward Ferrous Metals, Barrow 1/89.

DX 68026   DB 965491   CB 8   D8 012 1972
Matisa D8 Consolidator allocated to the Watford Division. Converted at Newton Heath RCE Works in 1980 to an inspection trolley and allocated to Newtown. Sold from Newtown to Blackman, Soldridge 5/86. Resold to Mid-Hants Railway 8/86.

DX 68027   DB 965473   CB 2   D8 002 1970
Matisa D8 Consolidator allocated to the Bimingham Division. Converted at Newton Heath RCE Works in 1980 to an inspection trolley and allocated to Newtown. Sold from Newtown to Blackman, Soldridge 5/86 and scrapped at Soldridge 8/86.

DX 68028   DB 965391   MCM 71/1   D8 004 1971
Matisa D8 Consolidator allocated to the Scottish Pool. Converted at Kilmarnock Works in 1977 to an inspection trolley and initially allocated to Georgemas Jn. Later Crianlarich. Scrapped at Kilmarnock RCE Workshops by Hepburn, Coatbridge 5/88.

DX 68029   DB 965393   MCM 71/3   D8 011 1971
Matisa D8 Consolidator allocated to the Glasgow South Division. Converted at Kilmarnock Works in 1978 to an inspection trolley and allocated to Spean Bridge. Later Crianlarich. Scrapped at Kilmarnock RCE Workshops by Hepburn, Coatbridge 5/88.

DX 68037   DB 965104   DE 320522   7619 1957
Type 17A Wickham trolley initially delivered to York. Allocated to Richmond. Scrapped at Darlington ODM Depot by a private contractor 12/81.

DX 68040   DB 965954   –   10650 1972
Wickham purpose built 2 ton trailer initially delivered to York and allocated to Castleford, Woolley, Huddersfield. Later Haltwhistle and Hexham. Sold to a private contractor for scrap and removed from site at Haltwhistle 8/87.

DX 68041   DB 965955   –   10651 1972
Wickham purpose built 2 ton trailer initially delivered to York and allocated to Skellow. Later Stanningley from where sold to the Upwell Fen Light Railway, Upwell near Wisbech 12/89.

DX 68050   –   TR 1   6872 1954
Type 4B Wickham trolley initially delivered to the GWR as PWM 2778. Allocated to Welshpool and later Hanwood from where it was sold to the Kent & East Sussex Railway 5/82.

DX 68051   –   TR 6   6901 1954
Type 4B Wickham trolley initially delivered to the GWR. Allocated to Caersws and later Llanbryn-mair from where it was sold to the Llangollen Railway Society 2/82. Resold to Peak Rail, Buxton 7/83. To Peak Rail, Darley Dale 4/88.

DX 68052   –   TR 11   4164 1948
Type 8S Wickham trolley initially delivered to the GWR as PWM 2187. Allocated to Portmadoc. Later Afon Wen and Harlech. Sold from Bangor to J Craven, Walesby, Newark 8/86.

DX 68053   –   TR 13   4166 1948
Type 8S Wickham trolley initially delivered to the GWR as PWM 2189. Allocated to Machynlleth from where it was sold to the Gloucestershire-Warwickshire Railway 5/82.

DX 68054   –   TR 16   6936 1955
Type 27 Wickham trolley initially delivered to the GWR as PWM 3951. Allocated to Hanwood and Welshpool. Sold from Bangor to the Bluebell Railway 8/86.

DX 68055   –   TR 18   7504 1956
Type 27 Mk III Wickham trolley initially delivered to Oxford as PWM 4301. Later allocated to Afon Wen, Borth, Machynlleth and Aberystwyth. Sold from Bangor to the Narrow Gauge Railway Centre of North Wales, Gloddfa Ganol, Blaenau Ffestiniog 8/86.

DX 68056   –   TR 19   7505 1956
Type 27 Mk III Wickham trolley initially allocated to Oxford as PWM 4302. Later allocated to Machynlleth. Sold from Bangor to M Jacob at the Midland Railway Centre 5/82. Resold to the Narrow Gauge Railway Centre of North Wales, Gloddfa Ganol, Blaenau Ffestiniog.

DX 68057   –   TR 20   7513 1956
Type 27 Mk III Wickham trolley initially delivered to Shrewsbury as PWM 4310. Allocated to Welshpool, Hanwood and later Llanbrynmair. Sold from Bangor to the Bluebell Railway 8/86.

DX 68058   –   TR 21   7514 1956
Type 27 Mk III Wickham trolley initially delivered to Shrewsbury as PWM 4311. Allocated to Harlech and latterly Machynlleth. Sold from Bangor to the Narrow Gauge Railway Centre of North Wales, Glodffa Ganol, Blaenau Festiniog 10/86.

DX 68059   –   TR 22   7515 1956
Type 27 Mk III Wickham trolley initially delivered to Shrewsbury as PWM 4312. Allocated to Portmadoc and later Barmouth from where it was sold to K. D. Harrison, Fencote Old Station 5/82. Resold to the Mid-Hants Railway.

DX 68060   DB 965567   TR 23   7516 1956
Type 27 Mk III Wickham trolley initially delivered to Shrewsbury as PWM 4313. Allocated to Aberdovey and late the Holyhead Breakwater line. Final allocation Llanrwyst to assist in flood damage repairs. Sold from Bangor to the Gloucestershire-Warwickshire Railway 5/82.

DX 68061   –   TR 26   4131 1947
Type 17A Wickham trolley initially delivered to the GWR as PWM 2214. Converted 6/61 to narrow gauge for use on the Vale of Rheidol line. Sold from Bangor to the Old Kiln Light Railway, Tilford near Farnham 8/86.

DX 68062   –   TR 34   8272 1959
Type 27 Mk III Wickham trolley. Allocated to Borth, Welshpool and later Hanwood. Sold from Bangor to the Midland Railway Centre 8/86.

DX 68063   DB 965562   TR 36   6885 1954
Type 4B Wickham trolley initially delivered to the GWR as PWM 2786. Allocated to Barmouth from where it was sold to the Telford Horsehay Steam Trust 5/82.

DX 68064   DB 965563   TR 37   6896 1954
Type 4B Wickham trolley initially delivered to the GWR as PWM 2797. Allocated to Newtown from where sold to the Stour Valley Railway 5/82.

DX 68065   –   TR 38   6643 1953
Type 27 Mk III Wickham trolley initially delivered to Haford Yard, Swansea as PWM 3764. Weed-Killer Trolley in Liverpool District 1975. Later Machynlleth from where sold to the East Somerset Railway 5/82.

DX 68066   DB 965564   TR 39   7509 1956
Type 27 Mk III Wickham trolley initially delivered to Circencester as PWM 4306. Mainly allocated to Caersws. Sold from Bangor to the Bluebell Railway 8/86.

DX 68067   DB 965565   TR 40   7517 1956
Type 27 Mk III Wickham trolley initially delivered to Shrewsbury as PWM 4314. Allocated to Llanbrymair. Sold from Bangor to K. D. Harrison, Fencote Old Station 5/82.

DX 68068   DB 965566   TR 41   4168 1948
Type 8S Wickham trolley initially delivered to the GWR as PWM 2191. Allocated to Borth from where sold to the Narrow Gauge Railway Centre of North Wales, Gloddfa Ganol, Blaenau Ffestiniog 5/82. Resold to the Bodmin and Wenford Railway Society.

DX 68072   –   DS 3232   6471 1952
2 Ton trailer converted at Stewarts Lane in 1975/6 from DS 3232, a Wickham Type 17A trolley initially delivered to Kingsworthy. Final allocation as a trolley was Norwood. As a trailer it was always allocated to Brighton. Broken up at Brighton by BR 6/86.

DX 68077   –   DS 3304   7823 1957
2 ton trailer converted at Stewarts Lane in 1975/6 from Type 27 Mk III Trolley DS 54, a Wickham Trolley initially delivered to Preston Park. As a trailer it was allocated to Redhill and Purley until scrapped at Stewarts Lane 12/82.

DX 68085   –   DS 3323   6654 1953
2 ton trailer converted at Stewarts Lane in 1976 from type 27 Mk III Trolley DS 3323 a Wickham Trolley initially delivered to Exeter St. Davids. As a trailer it was allocated to Sandown IoW until 5/79 when it is believed to have been scrapped by Valvona, Ryde.

DX 68092   DB 966036   –   10844 1975
Type 18 Mk VI Wickham trolley delivered to Three Bridges and allocated to Earlswood. Later Redhill. Badly damaged in an accident at Redhill 6/87. Remains disposed of from Stewarts Lane 1/89.

DX 68093   DB 965143   –   7974 1958
2 ton trailer converted at Stewarts Lane in 1976 from type 27A Mk III Trolley DB 965143, a Wickham Trolley initially delivered to Warminster. Later Eastleigh. Find allocation as a trolley was Purley. As a trailer it was allocated to Earlswood, Redhill and Merstham. Sold to a private contractor for scrap and removed from site at Redhill 4/90.

DX 68096   –   DB 965963   10704 1973
2 ton Wickham trailer which was always allocated to Brighton. Broken up at Brighton by BR 6/86.

Personnel Carriers (Various Manufacturers)

Current Stock:

DX 68800	–	–	001 1985	Newtown
DX 68801	–	–	002 1985	Porthmadog
DX 68802	–	–	003 1985	Machynlleth
DX 68803	–	–	004 1985	Machynlleth
DX 68805	–	–	006 1986	Sevenoaks
DX 68806	–	–	007 1986	Sole Street
DX 68807	–	–	008 1986	Tonbridge East
DX 68808	–	–	009 1986	Ramsgate
DX 68809	–	–	010 1986	Hassocks
DX 68810	–	–	011 1986	Purley
DX 68811	–	–	001 1987	Dingwall
DX 68812	–	–	KYH 862X	Perth
DX 68813	–	–	A855 MUA	Dingwall

Vehicle no longer in stock:

DX 68804   –   –   005 1985
Narrow gauge Permaquip Personal Carrier allocated to the Vale of Rheidol line and based at Aberystwyth. Sold to the Brecon Mountain Railway 3/89.

Bruff Road/Rail Mercedes 307D Personnel Carriers (DX 68901–6) and Permaquip Road/Rail Mercedes Lorries (DX 68907/8)

Current Stock:

DX 68901   –   –   E179 HUY   Dingwall

DX 68902	–	–	E192 JAB	Western Region
DX 68903	–	–	E193 JAB	Fort William
DX 68904	–	–	E710 GUY	Crianlarich
DX 68905	–	–	F653 RAB	Scottish Region
DX 68906	–	–	F591 RWP	Bristol Ashton Gate
DX 68907	–	–	-	Exmouth Jn.
DX 68908	–	–	-	Stanningley

90XXX MATISA RECORDING TROLLEYS (ex-50XXX Series)

These trolleys can travel between 20 mph and 40 mph and can automatically assess the track to provide up to date track geometry. They record all faults and check all details of line level, cross levels and gauge. This is related to previous information so that rates of deterioration can be assessed.

As a result of the arrival of BR's own Track Recording Coach DB 999550, which can travel at up to 125 mph in train formation, the fleet of thirteen track recording trolleys was able to be substantially reduced. In 1987 the five active survivors were renumbered into the 90xxx series. Following the introduction in 1987/8 of the Class 150 Track Recording Unit the requirement for the five surviving trolleys ceased, although four still remain stored awaiting either further conversion or disposal. One possibility is that DX 90011 may be converted into a gauging unit.

Current Stock:

DX 90001(a)	DB 965333	TRN 50/10	PV6 629 1967	Shettleston OOU
DX 90006	DB 965413	TRN 50/02	PV6 613 1966	Walsall OOU
DX 90007	DB 965414	TRN 50/03	PV6 628 1967	Walsall OOU
DX 90011(b)	DB 965303	TRN 50/11	PV6 620 1967	Swindon RCE Stores OOU

(a) Originally allocated to the Western being numbered PWM 6581, and later DX 50011. Now taken over the number of the original Scottish Region trolley.

(b) Originally allocated to the Southern Region as DX 50013. Now taken over the number of DX 50011, originally on the Western Region.

Vehicles no longer in stock:

DX 50001   DB 965190   TRN 50/05   PV6 601 1961
Allocated to the Scottish Region. Stored since 1983 at York Leeman Road. Sold to Berry, Leicester for scrap and removed from site at York Leeman Road 1/88.

DX 50002   DB 965310   TRN 50/08   PV5 570 1957
Allocated to the Scottish Region. Stored since 1983 at York Leeman Road. Acquired by the National Railway Museum, York, in 1986.

DX 50003   DB 965167   TRN 50/01   PV5 591 1960
Allocated to the Eastern Region. Wheels removed at York Leeman Road, the remainder of the machine being scrapped at King, Snailwell 10/80.

DX 50004   DB 965170   TRN 50/13   PV5 593 1960
Allocated to the Eastern Region. Used in 1987 at York Leeman Road as a shunter. Sold to Berry, Leicester for scrap and removed from site at York Leeman Road 1/88.

DX 90005   DB 965337   TRN 50/09   PV6 627 1967
Allocated to the Eastern Region. After ceasing to be used for track recording it was used as a shunter at York Leeman Road, from where it was sold to the Llangollen Railway 9/89.

DX 50008   DB 965411   TRN 50/07   PV5 577 1957
Allocated to the London Midland Region. Stored since 1982 at York Leeman Road. Sold to Berry, Leicester for scrap and removed from site at York Leeman Road 1/88.

DX 50009   DB 965412   TRN 50/12   PV5 576 1957
Allocated to the London Midland Region. Stored since 1983 at York Leeman Road. Sold to Berry, Leicester for scrap and removed from site at York Leeman Road 1/88.

DX 50010   PWM 4786   TRN 50/04   PV5 581 19582
Allocated to the Western Region. Wheels removed at York Leeman Road, the remainder of the machine being scrapped at King, Snailwell 10/80.

DX 50012   DB 965164   TRN 50/06   PV5 590 1959
Allocated to the Southern Region. Stored since 1982 at York Leeman Road. Sold to Berry, Leicester for scrap and removed from site at York Leeman Road 1/88.

98XXX GENERAL PURPOSE MAINTENANCE VEHICLES

The description for this group of plant numbers was initially applied in 1985 to the 68XXX series, but following a regrouping of vehicle types in 1987, only the former DX 681XX, DX 682XX, DX 683XX, DX 685XX, DX 686XX and DX 687XX types of vehicles are now so classified. These types of vehicles were transferred into the 98XXX series by changing the first digit of each vehicle from a 6 to a 9.

The DX 981XX series provided the first examples of the new generation of trolleys, having comfortable enclosed cabs and a hydraulic lifting crane. In 1975 Plasser introduced their OBW 8 on the Southern Region, DX 98200 being the only vehicle in the DX 982XX series not to have its own trailer. In 1982/3 Plasser built three OBW 10 trolleys all with their own trailers, the latter two DX 98202/3 being referred to as GP-TRAMMs. These letters stand for General Purpose-Track Repair and Maintenance Machine. The main machine has an A suffix to its number, whilst the driving trailer has a B suffix to its number. The main machine has a cabin which can seat nine crew, in addition to the driver and pilotman in the driving cab, whilst another two crew, plus driver and pilotman, can travel in the trailer. The TRAMM can either be incorporated in a train formation or travel at a maximum speed of 45 mph under its own power. A 4½ tonne capacity hydraulic hoist is mounted on the body of the main machine. Amongst its various uses are the ability to carry to and from site up to six 60 ft lengths of rail, the ploughing of outer sleeper ends and ballast shoulders for the deposit of service rails and rail positioning. In 1984/5 Plasser built eight more TRAMMs for BR, with a further one in 1986. A further nine were built during 1988. As it is the intention that all TRAMMs should eventually be reportable to TOPS, 98213–21 are prefixed DR. There are no immediate plans to change the prefixes of those TRAMMs already in service.

The DX 983XX series is for the Geismar version of the GP-TRAMM, all five examples being allocated to the London Midland Region. The DX 984XX series is for miscellaneous vehicles. DX 98401 was built by Permaquip and is an underground maintenance vehicle whose function is to carry rail, sleepers, ballast and tunnel maintenance equipment to and from an underground line work site. DX 98401 is not meant to carry personnel other than the operator and is equipped with manually operated hoists and jibs for the loading of rail, sleepers etc. DX 98402 was converted at Kilmarnock RCE Workshops from Plasser RCM 100 Rail Changer DX 79001 and is known as a RAMM (Rail and Material Mover). DX 98403 was built by Permaquip and is a Materials Handling Tug, whilst DX 98404 is a Maintenance and Transport Unit and is similar to a TRAMM. Permaquip are building DX 98404 and it is expected to be in service by the spring of 1991.

The DX 985XX series is for the Plasser TASC-45 machines, seven of which were delivered in 1985. The letters TASC stand for Track and Service Car and these machines are smaller than the TRAMM and have no trailer. However, Geismar delivered to the Scottish Region in 1990 a ballast hopper, a three-way tipping trailer and eight rail transportation trolleys for use with the four Plasser Tasc-45 machines in Scotland. No separate CEPs numbers have yet been allocated.

The sole representative so far of the DX 986XX series is DX 98600 the prototype Permaquip BREV (Broken Rail Emergency Vehicle). DX 98600 is a highly compact unit which carries on board all the materials and equipment required to permit the rapid repair/replacement of defective rails. The vehicle is equipped with an extendable canopy so that repair work can continue under cover. The BREV can travel at up to 37½ mph on level track, or can be moved by road lorry using Permaquip's Tracess off-tracking technique.

The DX 987XX series is for Permaquip PCTs (Powered Canopy Trolleys), twelve examples having been acquired by British Rail. The PCT is a lightweight on-track machine which gives full protection to welds being formed using the thermit welding process and provides in one unit all the facilities, equipment and materials necessary for the rapid production of high quality welds. The PCT can be on and off tracked using the Permaquip Tracess system.

The DR 988XX series is for the Kershaw version of the GP-TRAMM, four examples having been purchased from America for delivery in early 1991.

As regards allocation, the base location is normally only given for the smaller machines, but it should be emphasised that as with the larger machines they will often be found anywhere in that particular civil engineering area.

Schöma Trolleys with Trailers (ex-681xx Series)

Current stock:

DX 98100	DB 966025	–	4016 1974	Crianlarich
(with trailer	DB 966026	–	4019 1974)	
DX 98101	DB 966027	–	4017 1974	Georgemas Jn.
(with trailer	DB 966028	–	4018 1974)	

Plasser and Theurer OBW 8/OBW 10/GP-TRAMM (ex-682xx Series)

Current Stock:

DX 98201A	–	–	52465A	1982	Glasgow (Stranraer)
DX 98201B	–	–	52465B	1982	Glasgow (Stranraer)
DX 98202A	–	–	52530A	1983	South Wales
DX 98202B	–	–	52530B	1983	South Wales
DX 98203A	–	–	52531A	1983	Crewe
DX 98203B	–	–	52531B	1983	Crewe
DX 98204A	–	–	52759A	1984	Glasgow (Rutherglen)
DX 98204B	–	–	52759B	1984	Glasgow (Rutherglen)
DX 98205A	–	–	52760A	1985	Watford
DX 98205B	–	–	52760B	1985	Watford
DX 98206A	–	–	52761A	1985	Bristol
DX 98206B	–	–	52761B	1985	Bristol
DX 98207A	–	–	52762A	1985	Southern SE
DX 98207B	–	–	52762B	1985	Southern SE
DX 98208A	–	–	52763A	1985	Exeter
DX 98208B	–	–	52763B	1985	Exeter
DX 98209A	–	–	52764A	1985	Southern Central
DX 98209B	–	–	52764B	1985	Southern Central
DX 98210A	–	–	52765A	1985	South Wales
DX 98210B	–	–	52765B	1985	South Wales
DX 98211A	–	–	52766A	1985	Southern SW
DX 98211B	–	–	52766B	1985	Southern SW
DX 98212A	–	–	52985A	1986	Scottish NE (Perth)
DX 98212B	–	–	52985B	1986	Scottish NE (Perth)
DR 98213A	–	–	53187A	1988	Scottish SE (Carstairs)
DR 98213B	–	–	53187B	1988	Scottish SE (Carstairs)
DR 98214A	–	–	53188A	1988	Scottish SE (Dunbar)
DR 98214B	–	–	53188B	1988	Scottish SE (Dunbar)
DR 98215A	–	–	53192A	1988	Southern Central
DR 98215B	–	–	53192B	1988	Southern Central
DR 98216A	–	–	53193A	1988	Southern SW
DR 98216B	–	–	53193B	1988	Southern SW
DR 98217A	–	–	53194A	1988	Southern SE
DR 98217B	–	–	53194B	1988	Southern SE
DR 98218A	–	–	53195A	1988	Southern SE
DR 98218B	–	–	53195B	1988	Southern SE
DR 98219A	–	–	53196A	1988	Southern Central
DR 98219B	–	–	53196B	1988	Southern Central
DR 98220A	–	–	53197A	1988	Southern SW
DR 98220B	–	–	53197B	1988	Southern SW
DR 98221A	–	–	53198A	1988	Reading
DR 98221B	–	–	53198B	1988	Reading

Vehicle no longer in stock:

DX 98200	DB 966030	–	419	1975

OBW 8 Trolley mainly allocated to the Southern Central Division. Short period on Southern SE Division. Finally Southern SW Division. Sold from Wimbledon West to the Dart Valley Railway 5/88.

Geismar GP-TRAMM (ex-683xx Series)

Current Stock:

DX 98300A	–	–	G.780.001	1985 Nottingham
DX 98300B				
DX 98301A	–	–	G.780.002	1985 Birmingham
DX 98301B				
DX 98302A	–	–	G.780.003	1985 Manchester
DX 98302B				
DX 98303A	–	–	G.780.004	1985 Crewe
DX 98303B				
DX 98304A	–	–	G.780.005	1985 Preston
DX 98304B				

Miscellaneous Maintenance Vehicles

Current Stock:

DX 98401	–	–	001	1987	Waterloo and City Line
DX 98402	–	–	8948	1979	Greenhill Jn.
					Rebuilt Kilmarnock 1987
DX 98403	–	–	TGV 005	1990	Kirkdale
DX 98404	–	–	MTU 001	1991	Kirkdale

Plasser and Theurer TASC-45 (ex-685xx Series)

Current Stock:

DX 98500	–	–	52788	1985	Crianlarich
DX 98501	–	–	52789	1985	Dingwall
DX 98502	–	–	52790	1985	Spean Bridge
DX 98503	–	–	52791	1985	Georgemas Jn.
DX 98504	–	–	52792	1985	Norwich
DX 98505	–	–	52793	1985	Sheffield Woodburn
DX 98506	–	–	52794	1985	Newcastle

Geismar Ballast Hopper
(to work with Plasser TASC-45)

Current Stock:

–	–	–	1153	1989	Scottish Region

Geismar Three-Way Tipping Trailer
(to work with Plasser TASC-45)

Current Stock:

–	–	–	2440	1989	Scottish Region

Geismar Rail Transportation Trolley

Current Stock:

–	–	–	88063/1	1988	Scottish Region
–	–	–	88063/2	1988	Scottish Region
–	–	–	88063/3	1988	Scottish Region
–	–	–	88063/4	1988	Scottish Region
–	–	–	88063/5	1988	Scottish Region
–	–	–	88063/6	1988	Scottish Region
–	–	–	88063/7	1988	Scottish Region
–	–	–	88063/8	1988	Scottish Region

Permaquip Broken Rail Emergency Vehicle (ex-686xx Series)

Current Stock:

DX 98600	–	–	001	1985	Crianlarich

Permaquip Powered Canopy Trolley (ex-687xx Series)

Current Stock:

DX 98700	–	–	001	1985	Walsall
DX 98701	–	–	003	1986	Walsall
DX 98702	–	–	007	1986	Walsall
DX 98703	–	–	008	1986	Northampton
DX 98704	–	–	002	1986	Perth
DX 98705	–	–	004	1986	Shettleston
DX 98706	–	–	010	1986	Shettleston
DX 98707	–	–	012	1986	Perth
DX 98708	–	–	006	1986	Brockenhurst
DX 98709	–	–	005	1986	Pilning
DX 98710	–	–	011	1986	Aldershot
DX 98711	–	–	009	1986	Pilning

Kershaw CCT 45/10 TRAMM

Current Stock:

DR 98801	–	–	118	1990	Stratford or Norwich
DR 98802	–	–	119	1990	Stratford or Norwich
DR 98803	–	–	120	1990	Southern SE
DR 98804	–	–	121	1990	Glasgow (West Highland line)

◀Vintage Wickham trolley DX 68004 is pictured at Neath on 17th March 1988. DX 68004 has since been transfered to the Exeter civil engineering area.

Deryck W. Lewis

Geismar have supplied five GP TRAMMs to British Rail. This photograph shows DX 98301 passing through Longbridge station on 3rd December 1988.

Peter Tandy

TRACK MACHINES
72XXX BALLAST CONSOLIDATORS/TRACK STABILISERS

Ballast Consolidators were purchased from Matisa and Plasser in 1970–2 to follow tamping machines and so achieve the maximum stability condition. This was thought desirable because after squeeze tamping the ballast under the sleeper, the vibrating tamping tines are then with-drawn and lifted out of the ballast, leaving a loose ballast area.

The machines had heavy multi-consolidating pads mounted on vertical slides and vibrated by normal industrial electric vibrators in the case of Matisa and by rotating eccentric shafts driven by hydraulic motors in the case of Plasser. Vertical pressure is also applied. Normally eight consolidators are used per sleeper, one either side of the rail and each side of the sleeper. Shoulder consolidators are placed longitudinally, preferably to span three sleepers and in line with the crib consolidators.

Despite the fact that consolidation work was no longer considered essential almost all the Plasser Consolidators survived, being converted to mini-regulators. Seven of the Matisa Consolidators survived having been rebuilt as engineers trolleys.

In 1985 the Western Region modified DX 72017 so that it could be used for tunnel, bridge and platform gauging. DX 72020 was similarly modified at Westbourne Park, but is now scrapped. DX 72017 is still used for gauging work, whilst the other five surviving machines are all stored out of use on the Scottish Region.

The 722XX series is for dynamic track stabilisers and was first used in 1987. Plasser actually developed the dynamic track stabiliser in the 1970s, 07-32 DR 73601 being equipped with a dynamic stabiliser wagon. Plasser's current DGS 62-N model is self propelled and was acquired in 1987 and following very successful trials on the Eastern Region with DR 72201 in September 1987, Inter-City agreed to finance the purchase of DR 72202–10. Network South East have sub-sequently purchased DR 72211–3.

The DGS 62-N has eight retractable flanged wheels slung under the centre of the machine which can be pressed down onto the rails by jacks with a total force of 32 tonnes. Smaller horizontal wheels grip the outside of the rails so that they can be vibrated laterally. One pass of the stabiliser has the same settling effect on ballast as 100,000 tonnes of normal rail traffic thus eliminating the need for temporary speed restrictions following track work. DR 72201–13 are allocated to cover principal Inter-City routes where a reduction in the number of temporary speed restrictions yields the greatest commercial benefits.

Plasser and Theurer VDM 800U Consolidator

Current Stock:

Note: All vehicles were later converted to mini-regulators. DX 72017/20 were further modified to gauging machines.

DX 72000	DB 965904	PCM 70/1	59 1970	Kilmarnock OOU
DX 72002	DB 965906	PCM 71/3	85 1970	Slateford OOU
DX 72003	DB 965907	PCM 71/4	88 1970	Kilmarnock OOU
DX 72004	DB 965908	PCM 71/5	81 1971	Slateford OOU
DX 72017	–	PWM 7226	61 1970	South Wales
DX 72023	DB 965372	–	97 1971	Rutherglen OOU

Vehicles no longer in stock:

Note: DX 72001/7/9/22 were never converted into mini-regulators.

DX 72001   DB 965905   PCM 70/2   63 1970
Allocated to the Scottish SE Division. Stored OOU since the early 1970s at first Edinburgh Waver-ley Goods and later Slateford. Scrapped by Banknock Services, Denny, Stirling 1/85.

DX 72005   DB 965338   70/001   57 1970
Allocated to the Newcastle Squadron. Later Doncaster Squadron. Finally Norwich Division. Scrapped at Hitchin by Berry, Leicester 7/89.

DX 72006   DB 965345   70/002   62 1970
Allocated to the Stratford Division. Later Leeds Division. Scrapped at York Skelton by Berry, Leicester 10/85.

DX 72007   DB 965346   70/003   64 1970
Allocated to the York Division. Stored OOU at York since Mid-1970s. Scrapped at York Leeman Road by Hampton, Keele 6/83.

Originally built by Plasser as a consolidater DX 72017 is now in use as a gauging unit. This photograph shows DX 72017 at Worcester on 24th March 1990.   Stephen Widdowson

Sponsored by Inter City and Network South East repectively, Plasser Dynamic Track Stabilisers DR 72204/13 are seen at Hitchin on 24th July 1988.   Roy Hennefer

DX 72008   DB 965356   70/005   84 1970
Allocated to the Stratford Division. Scrapped at Romford by Texas Metal Industries, Hyde 7/85.

DX 72009   DB 965357   70/006   83 1970
Allocated to the Doncaster Division. Stored OOU at Doncaster since mid-1970s. Scrapped at Barlow CCE Tip by Hampton, Keele 8/82.

DX 72010   DB 965358   70/007   87 1970
Allocated to the Doncaster Squadron. Later Newcastle Division. Scrapped at Newcastle (Forth Banks) by Thompson, Stockton 6/89.

DX 72011   DB 965472   CB 1   55 1970
Allocated to the Nottingham Division. Scrapped at Derby Etches Park by Texas Metal Industries, Hyde 6/86.

DX 72013   DB 965482   CB 6   86 1970
Allocated to the Preston Division. Scrapped at Carlisle Upperby by Texas Metal Industries, Hyde 8/85.

DX 72014   DB 965483   CB 4   69 1970
Allocated to the Manchester Division. Sold from Guide Bridge to the Midland Railway Trust, Butterley 3/89.

DX 72015   DB 965484   CB 5   80 1970
Allocated to the Crewe Division. To Nottingham Division 1985. Scrapped at Derby (Slums Sidings) by Maize Metals, Wednesbury 9/89.

DX 72016   DB 965490   CB 3   65 1970
Allocated to the Preston Division. Scrapped at Carlisle Upperby by Ward Ferrous Metals, Chepstow 7/86.

DX 72018   –   PWM 7249   66 1970
Initially allocated to the Newport Division. Later Reading Division. Scrapped at Southall by Cartwright, Tipton 12/84.

DX 72019   –   PWM 7250   71 1970
Allocated to the Newport Division. Later Swansea Division. Scrapped at Carmarthen by Rollason, Telford 7/89.

DX 72020   –   PWM 7251   82 1971
Allocated to the Swansea Division. To Bristol Division 1978. Later Reading Division. Converted at Westbourne Park in 1986 to a gauging machine. Scrapped at Reading by Phillips (Metals), Llanelli 2/89.

DX 72021   DB 965370   –   95 1971
Allocated to the Southern SW Division. Transferred to the Scottish Region 1978. Allocated to the Scottish SE Division. Scrapped at Kilmarnock RCE Workshops by Hepburn, Coatbridge 5/88.

DX 72022   DB 965371   –   96 1971
Allocated to the Southern Central Division. Stored OOU at Stewarts Lane since mid-1970s. Scrapped at Stewarts Lane by British Contractors Plant, Staines 11/80.

DX 72024   DB 965373   –   98 1971
Allocated to the Southern SE Division. Later Southern Central Division. Transferred to the Western Region. Allocated to the Exeter Division. Scrapped at Plymouth Tavistock Jn. by Rollason, Telford 3/89.

Matisa D8 Consolidator

Current Stock (Machines rebuilt as Inspection Trolleys):

CEPS Number	DB 96XXXX Number	Regional Identity	Works Number	Trolley Number	Place of Conversion
DX 72100	DB 965391	MCM 71/1	004 1971	DX 68028	Kilmarnock RCE Works 1977
DX 72101	DB 965575	MCM 72/1	014 1972	DX 68031	Kilmarnock RCE Works 1981
DX 72102	DB 965393	MCM 71/3	011 1971	DX 68029	Kilmarnock RCE Works 1978
DX 72104	DB 965369	70/008	005 1971	DX 68030	Kilmarnock RCE Works 1979
DX 72107	DB 965392	CB 10	006 1971	DX 68025	Newton Heath RCE

Pictured near Abbotswood Jn. on 5th February 1990 whilst en route to Worcester are Plasser 07-16 DR 73222 and Plasser 07-275 DR 73305. DR 73222 is the machine in the foreground.
Stephen Widdowson

Plasser lightweight single-axle 08-16/90 No. DR 73501 is pictured at Loughborough on 26th August 1989.
Paul Biggs

| DX 72109 | DB 965491 | CB 8 | 012 1972 | DX 68026 | Newton Heath RCE Works 1980 |
| DX 72115* | DB 965473 | CB 2 | 002 1970 | DX 68027 | Newton Heath RCE Works 1980 |

Note: DX 72115 was incorrectly renumbered DX 72012 in 1975.

Vehicles no longer in stock:

DX 72103   DB 965347   70/004   001 1970
Allocated to the York Division. Stored at York since mid-1970s. Broken up at York Warehouse Yard by BR 1/81.

DX 72105   DB 965363   70/009   009 1971
Allocated to the Newcastle Squadron. Stored at York since mid-1970s. Broken up at York Warehouse Yard by BR 1/81.

DX 72106   DB 965386   70/010   013 1972
Allocated to the Newcastle Squadron. Stored at York since mid-1970s. Broken up at York Warehouse Yard by BR 1/81.

DX 72108   DB 965481   CB 7   008 1971
Allocated to the Birmingham Division. Stored OOU at Tyseley since mid-1970s. Scrapped at Tyseley by Texas Metals, Hyde 8/83.

DX 72110   DB 965933   CB 9   016 1972
Initially allocated to the Liverpool Division. Later Preston Division. Scrapped at Preston Lostock Hall by Jackson, Blackpool 4/83.

DX 72111   –   PWM 7245   003 1971
Allocated to the Bristol Division. To Westbourne Park in 1978 for possible conversion to a trolley. Scrapped at Westbourne Park by Round, Wednesbury 12/80.

DX 72112   –   PWM 7246   010 1971
Allocated to the Gloucester Division. To Westbourne Park in 1978 for possible conversion to a trolley. Scrapped at Westbourne Park by Round, Wednesbury 12/80.

DX 72113   –   PWM 7247   007 1971
Allocated to the Plymouth Division. To Westbourne Park in 1978 for possible conversion to a trolley. Scrapped at Westbourne Park by Round, Wednesbury 12/80.

DX 72114   –   PWM 7248   015 1972
Allocated to the Taunton Division. To Westbourne Park in 1978 for possible conversion to a trolley. Scrapped at Westbourne Park by Round, Wednesbury 12/80.

Plasser and Theurer Dynamic Track Stabiliser

Current Stock:

DR 72201	–	–	253 1987	Newcastle
DR 72202	–	–	260 1987	Crewe
DR 72203	–	–	261 1988	Reading
DR 72204	–	–	262 1988	Peterborough
DR 72205	–	–	263 1988	Newcastle
DR 72206	–	–	264 1988	Scottish SE
DR 72207	–	–	265 1988	Preston
DR 72208	–	–	266 1988	Doncaster
DR 72209	–	–	267 1988	Bristol
DR 72210	–	–	268 1988	Watford
DR 72211	–	–	270 1988	Southern Central
DR 72212	–	–	271 1988	Southern SE
DR 72213	–	–	272 1988	Stratford/Norwich

73XXX TAMPERS/LINERS

The introduction in 1987/8 of four new types of machines in the 73XXX group of plant of numbers has resulted in the second use of the 730XX, 731XX and 735XX series of numbers. The notes below are arranged in the order in which the different numbering series have been allocated, whilst the lists of machines are presented numerically.

Tamping/Lining machines carry out the two main functions of packing the track to its correct longitudinal and transverse level and pulling the track to correct alignment both on the straight and on transition and circular curves. The essential features of the machine are the tamping banks and the combined lifting and lining carriage.

The SLC machines (730XX) were the first to combine both functions, whilst the CTM machines (731XX) that followed also included the consolidating function, but it was found that the consolidating cycle slowed the other two operations and this series of machines was dropped. The original CTMs had an exposed front control position, but a second cab was added – with full length roof over the machine – and the original cab had the walls raised to provide sufficient standing headroom. The rear engine cover was at the same time reduced in size to improve visibility. The only survivor of these two series is DX 73116 which had been converted to the prototype stoneblower.

The next series of machines the 07 (732XX) were designed around frames of full vehicle length. These machines have full vehicle equipment and are equipped with automatic gearboxes and are powerful enough to tow other civil engineering machines. Comfortable cabins are provided at each end with contoured seats, inter-com system and heaters. British Rail has had six series of these machines, each series incorporating improvements over the previous one. Series one machines are DR 73200/1/5/6/8/11-3, Series two are DR 73202–4/7/9/10, Series three are DR 73214–27, Series four are DR 73228–37 (with DR 73237 incorporating the Long Chord Lining System and equipped with a trailer), Series five are DR 73238–72 whilst Series six are DR 73273–9.

At the end of 1982 the Southern Region became the first region to withdraw 07s from service when it condemned DR 73211–3. Although DR 73211 was scrapped in 1984, DR 73212/3 were reprieved being transferred to the Scottish and Eastern Regions respectively. In 1986 DR 73200 was scrapped, whilst in 1987 DR 73201/13 were disposed of. The arrival of six 09–32 CSMs in 1988 enabled the remaining Series one and Series two machines (with the exception of DR 73203) to be withdrawn. In addition a number of Series three and Series four machines were condemned. During 1989/90 DR 73271 has been used for testing ATA (The Automatic Track Top and Alignment System) and fourteen 07s have now been equipped with that system.

The 733XX series are similar to the plain line tamping/lining machines but in order to deal adequately with the weight of points and crossing work, the output of the engine of these machines is much greater and the lifting capacity and the lining force are greater. The layout of the equipment is different, whilst they are in addition fitted with twin operators cabins and control positions located directly over each rail at a low level, so that the operators have a clear view of the sleeper to be tamped, and of the lifting equipment. DR 73300 is a Series one, whilst DR 73301/2 are Series three, DR 73303–5 are Series four, DR 73306–11 are Series five and DR 73312 is a Series six. DR 73313–6 are Series seven, whilst DR 73317–21 are Series eight, this type all having an integrated material wagon.

DR 73300/2 are the only 07-275s that have been scrapped. In 1987 a former London underground switch and crossing tamper was acquired as a source of spares, although it would have been allocated CEPS number DR 73322, if it had been economically viable to reinstate it for further use.

The 734XX series is for tampers which have 32 tools instead of the more general 16 tines. The 32 tool machines tamp two sleepers at a time, but the performance improvement is not as great as might be thought because apart from the basic feature of two sleeper tamping the other times in the work cycle are the same as the single sleeper machine. DR 73400–5 are Series five whilst DR 73413–35 are Series six. DR 73400/2 are the only 07–32s that have been scrapped.

The first use of the 735XX series was for the only representative of Matisa whilst the 736XX series is for the 07-32 which is coupled to a dynamic stabiliser wagon.

The 737XX series has just one representative, the prototype production Pneumatic Ballast Injection machine, designated PBI 84. DR 73700 was completed in November 1984 and is a three bodied articulated vehicle powered by a Rolls Royce diesel engine. Equipped with its own hopper and grab unit, it can load and carry sufficient stone for a full working shift. The machine injects a measured quantity of ballast under each sleeper and after compaction the track is restored to the correct level. Tests have showed that track geometry can be maintained for a longer period after stone blowing than by standard mechanical tamping.

Following extensive trials and various modifications and adjustments, it is now the intention to have a fleet of Stoneblowers primarily for use on high speed lines. Purchase will be through competitive tender with the first fleet machine due for delivery in June 1992. There will be a six months evaluation period following which, if successful, further orders will be placed, the first order being for seven machines.

The experience accumulated through the different series of Plasser 07 machines resulted in the development of the 08 series, DR 73801/2 being the two machines acquired by British Rail at the end of 1984. DR 73801/2 were initially numbered in the 07 series as DR 73280/1. The progress made in electronics, hydraulics and engineering construction has been applied to the 08 series machines, which in addition have an integrated material wagon. The 739XX series was first used in 1987 when two 08-275 Switch and Crossing machines were acquired, a third machine being purchased in 1988.

In 1987 the purchase of an 09-16 CSM and an 09-32 CSM resulted in the second use of the 730XX and 731XX series of numbers, DR 73001 and DR 73101 being the numbers allocated. A further six 09-32 CSMs were purchased and DR 73102–7 entered service in 1988. On the 09-CSM the tamping heads are not mounted on the machine itself, but carried on a subframe with its own wheels for guidance and partial support. The 09-CSM moves forward at a constant pace, only the tamping subframe is accelerated and decelerated within each tamping cycle. As conventional tampers have to be accelerated and braked sharply within each working cycle, the 09-CSM saves not only energy but reduces mechanical stresses on the machine as a whole.

The second use of the 735XX series is for DR 73501 a Plasser lightweight, single axle 08-16/90 tamping machine incorporating all the latest features and which entered service in 1988.

Further lightweight, single axle machines are due to be delivered in 1991 and details of these can be found in the 75xxx series which is to be used for the second time in order that mid-range machines can be grouped together in the same numbering series.

Plasser and Theurer 09-16 CSM Tamper/Liner

Current Stock:

DR 73001   –   –   2340 1987   Leeds

Plasser and Theurer 06-32 SLC Tamper/Liner
(First use of 730XX number series)

Vehicles no longer in stock:

DX 73000   DB 965725   PSLC 68/1   695 1968
Allocated to the Glasgow South Division. Scrapped at Kilmarnock RCE Workshops by Cohen, Motherwell 6/81

DX 73001   DB 965732   PSLC 68/2   702 1968
Allocated to the Scottish SE Division. Scrapped at Kilmarnock RCE Workshops by a private contractor in 1982.

DX 73002   DB 965736   PSLC 69/3   706 1968
Allocated to the Scottish NE Division. Scrapped at Kilmarnock RCE Workshops by a private contractor in 1982.

DX 73003   DB 965741   PSLC 69/4   711 1969
Allocated to the Glasgow North Division. Scrapped at Kilmarnock RCE Workshops by Cohen, Motherwell 6/81.

DX 73004   DB 965727   73/001   697 1968
Allocated to the Kings Cross Division. To Hitchin for stripping 4/78, scrapped at Hitchin by Berry, Leicester 7/79.

DX 73005   DB 965729   73/002   699 1968
Initially allocated to the Doncaster Squadron. Later York Division. Scrapped at Malton by Cartwright, Tipton 5/83.

DX 73006   DB 965731   73/003   701 1968
Allocated to the Newcastle Squadron. To Hitchin for stripping 7/78. Scrapped at Hitchin by Hermagen (Plant Hire & Excavation), Tamworth 1/80.

DX 73007   DB 965734   73/004   704 1968
Allocated to the Newcastle Squadron. Scrapped at Newcastle (Forth Goods) by Ward, Sheffield 10/78.

DX 73008   DB 965738   73/005   708 1969
Allocated to the Stratford Division. Scrapped at Hitchin by Miller, Downham Market 1/84.

DX 73009   DB 965739   73/006   709 1969
Allocated to the Stratford Division. Later Doncaster Division. Scrapped at York Leeman Road by Booth, Rotherham 10/85.

DX 73010   DB 965742   73/007   712 1969
Initially allocated to the Cambridge Squadron. Later Sheffield Division. Acquired by the National Railway Museum York 8/85.

DX 73011   DB 965743   73/008   713 1969
Allocated to the York Squadron. Later Newcastle Division. Scrapped at Ferryhill by Round, Wednesbury 10/83.

DX 73012   DB 965724   SLC 1   694 1968
Allocated to the Watford Division. To Hitchin for stripping 10/78. Scrapped at Hitchin by Round, Wednesbury 6/80.

DX 73013   DB 965726   SLC 2   696 1968
Allocated to the Watford Division. Later Manchester Division. Scrapped at Guide Bridge by Chadwick, Stalybridge 4/83.

DX 73014   DB 965728   SLC 3   698 1968
Allocated to the Nottingham Division. Later Manchester Division. Scrapped at Guide Bridge by Texas Metals, Hyde 9/83.

DX 73015   DB 965730   SLC 4   700 1968
Allocated to the Crewe Division. Broken up at Crewe ETD by BR 1/79.

DX 73016   DB 965733   SLC 5   703 1968
Allocated to the Manchester Division. Condemned in 1983 and moved to the RCE Track Machine School, Briar Hill, Northampton where it was used to train new machine operators in fire fighting. Scrapped at Briar Hill, Northampton by Maize Metals, Wednesbury 7/90.

DX 73017   DB 965735   SLC 6   705 1968
Allocated to the Liverpool Division. Later Manchester Division. Scrapped at Guide Bridge by Texas Metals, Hyde 8/83.

DX 73018   DB 965737   SLC 7   707 1968
Allocated to the Birmingham Division. Later Manchester Division. Scrapped at Guide Bridge by Texas Metals, Hyde 9/83.

DX 73019   DB 965740   SLC 8   710 1969
Allocated to the Preston Division. Later Manchester Division. Scrapped at Guide Bridge by Chadwick, Stalybridge 4/83.

Plasser and Theurer 09-32 CSM Tamper/Liner

Current Stock:

DR 73101	–	–	2339 1987	Peterborough
DR 73102	–	–	2375 1988	Watford
DR 73103	–	–	2376 1988	Preston
DR 73104	–	–	2377 1988	Reading
DR 73105	–	–	2378 1988	Crewe
DR 73106	–	–	2379 1988	Bristol
DR 73107	–	–	2380 1988	Scottish SE

Plasser and Theurer 06-16 CTM
(First use of 731XX number series)

Current Stock:
DX 73116   –   PWM 7258   U2097 1970   Derby Technical Centre

Note: DX 73116 was converted by Derby Technical Centre into a 'Stoneblower'.

Vehicles no longer in stock:

DX 73100   DB 965912   PMUT 70/1   U2088 1970
Initially allocated to the Scottish Pool. Transferred to Glasgow South Division 1975. Scrapped at Kilmarnock RCE Workshops by Hepburn, Coatbridge 2/79.

DX 73101   DB 965913   PMUT 71/2   U2108 1970
Initially allocated to the Scottish Pool. Transferred to Glasgow South Division 1975. Scrapped at Kilmarnock RCE Workshops by Hepburn, Coatbridge 2/79.

DX 73102   DB 965914   PMUT 71/3   U2109 1970
Initially allocated to the Scottish Pool. Transferred to Glasgow South Division 1975. Scrapped at Kilmarnock RCE Workshops by Hepburn, Coatbridge 2/79.

DX 73103   DB 965915   PMUT 71/4   U2115 1970
Initially allocated to Scottish SE Division. Scrapped at Kilmarnock RCE Workshops by Burnett and Cairns, Dalkeith 3/80.

DX 73104   DB 965916   PMUT 71/5   U2117 1970
Initially allocated to Scottish NE Division. Transferred to Glasgow South Division 1975. Scrapped at Kilmarnock RCE Workshops by Hepburn, Coatbridge 2/79.

DX 73105   DB 965350   74/100   U2098 1970
Allocated to the York Squadron. Scrapped at Barlow RCE Tip by Howard and Pepperell, Sheffield 5/80.

DX 73106   DB 965351   74/101   U2092 1970
Allocated to the Newcastle Squadron. Scrapped at Barlow RCE Tip by Ward, Sheffield 11/79.

DX 73107   DB 965352   74/102   U2106 1970
Initially allocated to the Cambridge Squadron. Later York Squadron. Scrapped at Barlow CCE Tip by Hampton, Keele 8/82.

DX 73108   DB 965353   74/103   U2113 1970
Initially allocated to the Doncaster Squadron. To Hitchin for stripping 6/79. Scrapped at Hitchin by Round, Wednesbury 9/80.

DX 73109   DB 965362   74/104   U2090 1970
Initially allocated to the York Squadron. Loaned to Scottish SE Division 1979 to assist at Penmanshiel - scrapped at Tweedmouth by Brown, Coldstream 9/81.

DX 73110   DB 965486   CTM 1   U2104 1970
Initially allocated to the Watford Division. Later Crewe Division. To Derby Technical Centre 1979 to be a source of spares for the prototype stoneblower DX 73116. Scrapped at Derby Technical Centre by Ward Ferrous Metals, Ilkeston 10/85.

DX 73111   DB 965487   CTM 2   U2111 1970
Allocated to Crewe Division. Badly damaged in an accident at Colwich 2/80. Broken up at Crewe ETD by BR 8/80.

DX 73112   DB 965488   CTM 3   U2112 1970
Allocated to the Preston Division. To Derby Technical Centre 1979 to be a source of spares for the prototype stoneblower DX 73116. Scrapped at Derby Technical Centre by Ward Ferrous Metals, Ilkeston 10/85.

DX 73113   DB 965489   CTM 4   U2114 1970
Allocated to the Liverpool Division. To Plasser, West Ealing 1979, initially as a source of spares for the prototype stoneblower DX 73116. Now cut down and used as a test bed for sleeper positioning tests.

DX 73114   –   PWM 7256   U2094 1970
Allocated to the Newport Division. To Hitchin for stripping 12/78. Scrapped at Hitchin by Round, Wednesbury 9/80.

DX 73115   –   PWM 7257   U2101 1970
Allocated to the Reading Division. To Hitchin for Stripping 11/78. Scrapped at Hitchin by Round, Wednesbury 9/80.

DX 73117   DB 965928   PWM 7935   U2074 1970
Initially allocated to RCE Training School, Watford. To Bristol Division 1974. To Swansea Division 1976. To Hitchin for stripping 12/78. Scrapped at Hitchin by Round, Wednesbury 9/80.

DX 73118   DB 965365   –   U2100 1970
Allocated to the Southern SW Division. Scrapped at Wimbledon by Ward, Sheffield 12/79.

DX 73119   DB 965368   –   U2118 1970
Allocated to the Southern SE Division. Scrapped at Hither Green by Stanley, Bexleyheath 6/79.

DX 73120   DB 965367   –   U2119 1970
Allocated to the Southern SW Division. Scrapped at Eastleigh by Ward, Sheffield 11/79.

DX 73121   DB 965366   –   U2120 1970
Allocated to the Southern Central Division. Scrapped at Three Bridges by Hudson, Dudley 7/79.

Plasser and Theurer 07–16 Universal Tamper/Liner

Current Stock

DR 73203	DB 965960	74/110	1042 1973	Norwich
DR 73204	DB 965961	74/111	1043 1973	York Leeman Road OOU
DR 73205	DB 965374	TU 1	941 1971	Crewe Basford Hall Yard OOU
DR 73210	–	PWM 7728	1040 1973	Hitchin OOU
DR 73214	DB 965964	PWM 8043	1107 1973	Scottish NE
DR 73215	DB 965965	PWM 8044	1108 1973	Exeter
DR 73216	DB 965966	PWM 8045	1109 1974	South Wales

DR 73217	DB 965977	–	1120	1974	Scottish SE
DR 73218	DB 965967	–	1110	1974	Scottish NE
DR 73219	DB 965968	–	1111	1974	Kilmarnock OOU
DR 73220	DB 965969	PWM 8046	1112	1974	Reading
DR 73221	DB 965971	PWM 8047	1113	1974	Cardiff Cathays OOU
DR 73222	DB 965970	PWM 8048	1114	1974	Bristol
DR 73223	DB 965972	PWM 8049	1115	1974	Reading
DR 73224	DB 965973	PWM 8050	1116	1974	Bristol
DR 73225	DB 965974	–	1118	1974	Scottish NE (Inverness)
DR 73226	DB 965975	PWM 8051	1117	1974	Bristol
DR 73227	DB 965976	–	1119	1974	Glasgow
DR 73228	DB 965994	–	1200	1974	Cardiff Cathays –Yard shunter
DR 73229	DB 965995	–	1201	1974	Hitchin OOU
DR 73230	DB 965996	–	1202	1974	Westerleigh Training School
DR 73231	DB 965997	–	1203	1974	Crewe Gresty Road Primary Stores OOU
DR 73232	DB 965998	–	1204	1974	Bristol Marsh Jn. OOU
DR 73234	DB 966000	–	1212	1974	Rutherglen Training School
DR 73235	DB 966001	–	1213	1974	South Wales
DR 73236	DB 966002	–	1214	1974	Scottish SE
DR 73238	DB 966050	–	1455	1977	Newcastle
DR 73239	DB 966051	–	1456	1977	Preston
DR 73240	DB 966052	–	1457	1977	Manchester
DR 73241	DB 966053	–	1458	1977	Crewe
DR 73242	DB 966054	–	1459	1977	Kilmarnock OOU
DR 73243	DB 966055	–	1460	1977	Doncaster
DR 73244	DB 966056	–	1461	1977	Scottish SE
DR 73245	DB 966057	–	1462	1977	Birmingham
DR 73246	DB 966058	–	1479	1978	Southern SW
DR 73247	DB 966059	–	1463	1977	Stratford
DR 73248	DB 966060	–	1464	1977	Preston
DR 73249	DB 966061	–	1480	1978	Southern SE
DR 73250	DB 966062	–	1465	1977	Watford
DR 73251	DB 966063	–	1481	1978	Southern Central
DR 73252	DB 966064	–	1466	1977	Birmingham
DR 73253	DB 966065	–	1467	1977	Preston
DR 73254	DB 966066	–	1468	1977	Birmingham
DR 73255	DB 966067	–	1469	1977	Birmingham
DR 73256	DB 966068	–	1470	1977	Crewe
DR 73257	DB 966069	–	1482	1978	Southern Central
DR 73258	DB 966070	–	1471	1977	Manchester
DR 73259	DB 966071	–	1483	1978	Southern SE
DR 73260	DB 966072	–	1472	1977	Crewe
DR 73261	DB 966073	–	1484	1978	Southern SW
DR 73262	DB 966074	–	1473	1977	Crewe
DR 73263	DB 966075	–	1485	1978	Southern Central
DR 73264	DB 966076	–	1487	1978	Birmingham
DR 73265	DB 969072	–	1486	1978	Exeter
DR 73266	DB 969073	–	1488	1977	Northampton Training School
DR 73267	DB 969074	–	1489	1977	Nottingham
DR 73268	DB 969075	–	1490	1978	Glasgow
DR 73269	DB 969076	–	1491	1978	Nottingham
DR 73270	DB 969077	–	1492	1978	Nottingham
DR 73271	DB 969078	–	1493	1978	Derby Technical Centre
DR 73272	DB 969079	–	1494	1978	Nottingham
DR 73273	–	–	1543	1978	Merseyside
DR 73274	–	–	1544	1978	Merseyside
DR 73275	–	–	1545	1978	Watford
DR 73276	–	–	1546	1978	Southern SW
DR 73278	–	–	1548	1978	Southern SE
DR 73279	–	–	1549	1978	Southern SE

Note: DR 73280/1 were allocated in error to machines now numbered DR 73801/2 respectively.

Vehicles no longer in stock:

DR 73200   DB 965376   PO7T 72/1   946 1971
Initially allocated to the Glasgow North Division. Transferred to the Eastern Region 1981. Allocated to the Doncaster Division. Scrapped at Doncaster Marshgate by Berry, Leicester 5/86.

DR 73201   DB 965377   PO7T 72/2   947 1971
Initially allocated to the Glasgow North Division. Transferred to the Eastern Region 1981. Allocated to the Newcastle Division. To Doncaster Division 1985. Scrapped at Doncaster Marshgate by Maize Metals, West Bromwich 7/87.

DR 73202   DB 965957   PO7T 73/3   1041 1973
Allocated to the Glasgow South Division. Later Scottish Pool. To Glasgow North Division. Transferred to the London Midland Region 1982. Allocated to the Birmingham Division. Sold from Wolverhampton (Wednesfield Road) to the Midland Railway Trust, Butterley 1/90.

DR 73206   DB 965375   TU2   942 1971
Allocated to the Nottingham Division. To Birmingham Division 1988. Scrapped at Wolverhampton (Wednesfield Road) by Berry, Leicester 1/90.

DR 73207   DB 965574   TU4   1044 1973
Allocated to the Birmingham Division. Scrapped at Wolverhampton (Wednesfield Road) by Berry, Leicester 1/90.

DR 73208   DB 965378   PWM 7570   948 1972
Allocated to the Bristol Division. Transferred to RCE Training School, Watford 10/73. To Birmingham Division 1974. Transferred to the Eastern Region 1982. Allocated to the Leeds Division. Finally York HQ Training Section. Scrapped at Doncaster Marshgate by Berry, Leicester 6/88.

DR 73209   PWM 7727   1039 1972
Allocated to the Reading Division. Transferred to the Eastern Region 1982. Allocated to the Sheffield Division. Scrapped at Doncaster Marshgate by Berry, Leicester 6/88.

DR 73211   DB 965379   –   949 1972
Allocated to the Southern Central Division. Scrapped at Hitchin by Miller, Downham Market 1/84.

DR 73212   DB 965381   –   951 1972
Allocated to the Southern SE Division. Transferred to the Scottish Region 1983. Allocated to the Glasgow South Division. Scrapped at Rutherglen by Henderson Kerr, Mossend 6/88.

DR 73213   DB 965380   TU3   950 1972
Initially allocated to the London Midland Region. Transferred to the Southern Region 1973. Allocated to the Southern SW Division. Transferred to the Eastern Region 1983. Allocated to York HQ Training Section. Later Norwich Division. To Stratford Division 1985. Scrapped at Hitchin by Maize Metals, West Bromwich 11/87.

DR 73233   DB 965999   –   1211 1974
Allocated to the Swansea Division. Badly damaged in an accident at Landore 1987. Broken up at Cardiff Cathays by BR 12/88.

DR 73237   DB 966003   –   1215 1974
Allocated to the Reading Division. Broken up at Bristol Marsh Jn. (except for the cabin which is in use as a static store) by BR 2/89.

DR 73277   –   –   1547 1978
Allocated to the Southern Central Division where initially it was numbered in error DR 73410. Badly damaged in an accident at Eridge 6/88. Scrapped at Crowborough by Rollason, Telford 4/89.

Plasser and Theurer 07–275 Switch and Crossing Tamper/Liner

Current Stock

DR 73301	DB 965978	74/091	421 1973	Scottish NE
DR 73303	DB 966043	–	477 1975	Watford
DR 73304	DB 966048	–	505 1976	Stratford
DR 73305	DB 966047	–	504 1976	Bristol
DR 73306	DB 966083	–	530 1978	Glasgow
DR 73307	DB 966084	–	531 1978	Leeds
DR 73308	DB 966085	–	534 1978	Southern SW
DR 73309	DB 966086	–	532 1978	South Wales
DR 73310	DB 966087	–	533 1978	Newcastle

DR 73311	DB 966088	–	535 1978	Southern SE
DR 73312	–	–	615 1980	Reading
DR 73313	–	–	664 1981	Southern Central
DR 73314	–	–	665 1981	Peterborough
DR 73315	–	–	715 1983	Crewe
DR 73316	–	–	716 1983	Stratford
DR 73317	–	–	733 1984	Doncaster
DR 73318	–	–	734 1984	Norwich
DR 73319	–	–	744 1984	Watford
DR 73320	–	–	745 1984	Preston
DR 73321	–	–	746 1984	Scottish SE
–	–	–	465 1975	Rugby OOU

Vehicles no longer in stock:

DR 73300   DB 965931   SCT 1   387 1972
Initially allocated to the Birmingham Division. Transferred to Crewe Division 1985 to assist in the Crewe remodelling. Broken up at Crewe Gresty Road by BR 6/86.
DR 73302   DB 965979   74/092   422 1973
Initially allocated to the York HQ Section. Later Doncaster Division. Finally Sheffield Division. Scrapped at Hitchin by Williams, Hitchin 4/86.

Plasser and Theurer 07–32 Duomatic Tamper/Liner

Current Stock:

DR 73401	DB 966078	–	1474 1977	Watford
DR 73403	DB 966080	–	1476 1977	Watford
DR 73404	DB 966081	–	1477 1977	Newcastle
DR 73405	DB 966082	–	1478 1978	Preston
DR 73413	–	–	1560 1978	Merseyside
DR 73414	–	–	1561 1978	Bristol
DR 73415	–	–	1562 1978	Exeter
DR 73416	–	–	1563 1978	Reading
DR 73418	–	–	1565 1978	South Wales
DR 73419	–	–	1566 1978	South Wales
DR 73420	–	–	1567 1978	Doncaster
DR 73421	–	–	1568 1978	Scottish SE
DR 73422	–	–	1569 1978	Perth OOU
DR 73423	–	–	1570 1978	Scottish NE
DR 73424	–	–	1571 1978	Stratford
DR 73425	–	–	1572 1978	Scottish SE
DR 73426	–	–	1573 1978	Glasgow
DR 73427	–	–	1574 1978	Glasgow
DR 73428	–	–	1575 1978	Newcastle
DR 73429	–	–	1576 1978	York Training Section
DR 73430	–	–	1577 1978	Stratford
DR 73431	–	–	1578 1978	Peterborough
DR 73432	–	–	1579 1978	Leeds
DR 73433	–	–	1580 1978	Doncaster
DR 73434	–	–	1581 1978	Norwich
DR 73435	–	–	1582 1978	Peterborough

Notes:
DR 73406–DR 73412 were allocated in error to machines now numbered DR 73273–DR 73279 respectively.
DR 73417 was allocated in error to machine now numbered DR 73601.

Vehicles no longer in stock:

DR 73400   DB 966077   –   1450 1977
Allocated to the Scottish Pool. Transferred to the Eastern Region 3/82. Allocated to the Leeds Division. Loaned to Preston Division 1987. Scrapped at York Leeman Road by Howard and Wheeler, Ecclesfield 12/88.

DR 73402   DB 966079   –   1475 1977
Allocated to the Bristol Division. To Exeter Division 1982. Returned to Bristol Division 6/84. To Derby Technical Centre 1987. Damaged in an accident at Old Dalby 4/88. Scrapped at Nottingham Eastcroft by Berry, Leicester 1/90.

Plasser and Theurer 08–16/90 Tamper/Liner

Current Stock:

DR 73501   –   –   2381 1988   Nottingham

Matisa Tamper/Liner
(First use of 735XX number series)

Vehicle no longer in stock:

DR 73501   DB 966095   –   4970028 1978
Initially allocated to the York Squadron. Later York Division. Finally Sheffield Division. Sold to Berry, Leicester for scrap and removed from site at York Leeman Road 5/86.

Plasser and Theurer 07–32 with Dynamic Stabiliser Wagon

Current Stock:

DR 73601   –   –   1564 1978   Nottingham

Plasser and Theurer Pneumatic Ballast Injection Machine-PBI 84

Current Stock:

DR 73700   –   –   52705 1984   Derby Technical Centre

Plasser and Theurer 08–16 Universal Tamper/Liner

Current Stock:

DR 73801   –   –   2204 1984   Norwich
DR 73802   –   –   2205 1984   Newcastle

Plasser and Theurer 08–275 Switch and Crossing Tamper/Liner

Current Stock:

DR 73901   –   –   831 1987   Birmingham
DR 73902   –   –   832 1987   Bristol
DR 73903   –   –   854 1988   Manchester/Merseyside

74XXX TAMPERS

The basic feature of a tamping machine which has remained virtually unchanged for over 30 years is the tamping mechanism. There are two tamping 'banks' on each machine, one centred over each rail. The tamping bank, with tools vibrating, is lowered until the tools (inserted into the space at each side of the rail, both sides of the sleeper) are below sleeper base and the tools are then moved in towards the sleeper centre line – thus squeezing ballast under the sleeper. This closing action is by either screw mechanism or hydraulic rams. Machines have either 16 tines and tamp one sleeper at a time, or 32 tools are fitted (16 to a bank) and the machine is able to tamp two sleepers at once.

The first tampers were essentially work tools mounted on very simple low speed mobile carriages. Small trolley wheels were driven by roller chains to give a top speed of about 12 mph. The suspension was very elementary (sometimes only rubber blocks), manually applied transmission brakes were common and machines were of short wheelbase. The frames did not carry buffers or drawgear and the machines could not sustain buffing contact with standard railway vehicles. Operator accommodation was of a simple type-either no cab or a rudimentary one with steel tractor-type seats. The engines were four cylinder type of about 60 bhp.

On the early Matisa machines, the tamping mechanism was mounted between the axles on a short wheelbase, but only tamped a track already jacked to correct position. The Plasser machines, however had a short wheelbase, but the tamping and lift mechanism was cantilevered out from the front of the machine and counter balanced by the engine, fuel tanks and counterweights at the rear. The Plasser VKR 04, of which British Rail had 44, were the first machines to carry out lifting, levelling and tamping mechanically and automatically in one working operation. None survive on British Rail and none of the last survivors were ever allocated CEPS numbers. The next development was the Plasser VKR 05 which had roller lifting units, an infra-red levelling system and an enclosed work cabin. Eight examples of the first version were supplied to British Rail, although only three survived by the time the CEPS numbering scheme was introduced. The Scottish Region survivor became the only representative of the DX 74XXX series, as the Eastern Region survivors found themselves in the DX 741XX series. All the 05 machines and the 06–16 actually bore 05E on their worksplates. Twenty seven 05E machines were allocated in the DX 741XX series as this series of numbers included the two surviving 05 Eastern Region machines already referred to, plus the one MPT 195 acquired by British Rail.

The DX 742XX series was only represented by one machine, this being a VKR 06-16, a slightly improved version of the 05E. The DX 743XX series was allocated to the first Duomatic machines, these being the first machines to tamp two sleepers simultaneously. The first Duomatic units were fitted on the cantilever design machines of the VKR series. The DX 744XX series was allocated to the next batch of Plasser 06-32 machines, these being built for British Rail by Rolls Royce of Shrewsbury. The DX 745XX series was represented by just six machines, these being the first machines which could tamp the entire area of a switch and crossing. The lateral movement of the working units enables the tamping tools to be centred exactly over the tamping area. The lateral swivel of the tools permitted tamping of the wide parts of switches such as frogs, guard rails etc. Where there were obstacles on the ballast bed the individual tools could be swung outwards so that even awkward parts of the switch could be tamped. A clear view was afforded by the operators cabins located directly over the rail.

Finally in this section is the DX 746XX series, this being another series only represented by one machine, the Plasser Universal Joint tamper. The eighty-seven machines in this section have all been disposed of. The DX 74000, DX 74100 and DX 74200 series of numbers are being used for the second time – see Small Plant section.

Plasser and Theurer VKR 05 Tamper

Vehicle no longer in stock:

DX 74000   DB 965248   PMT 3D   377 1963
Allocated to the Glasgow North Division. Scrapped at Kilmarnock RCE Workshops by a private contractor in 1975.

Plasser and Theurer VKR 05E Tamper

Vehicles no longer in stock:

DX 74100   DB 965250   PMT 5D   443 1964

Allocated to the Scottish NE Division. Scrapped at Kilmarnock RCE Workshops by a private contractor in 1975.

DX 74101   DB 965251   PMT 6D   444 1964
Allocated to the Glasgow South Division. Badly damaged in an accident at Stewarton 11/74. Scrapped at Kilmarnock RCE Workshops by a private contractor in 1975.

DX 74102   DB 965252   PMT 7D   453 1964
Allocated to the Glasgow North Division. Scrapped at Crianlarich Upper by Burnett and Ure, Grangemouth 6/76.

DX 74103   DB 965253   PMT 8D   458 1964
Initially allocated to the Glasgow South Division. Later Glasgow North Division. Scrapped at Kilmarnock RCE Workshops by Berry, Leicester 12/77.

DX 74104   DB 965313   74/028   370 1963
Allocated to the Doncaster Division. Scrapped at Doncaster by Whitehead of? in 1977.

DX 74105   DB 965315   74/030   376 1963
Initially allocated to the Newcastle Division. Later Doncaster Division. Scrapped at Doncaster by a private contractor in 1977.

DX 74106   DB 965316   74/031   455 1964
Initially allocated to Norwich Division. Later Newcastle Division. Scrapped at Newcastle (Forth Goods) by Ward, Sheffield 11/79.

DX 74107   DB 965317   74/032   456 1964
Allocated to the Stratford Division. Scrapped at Ipswich by Garratt, Crewe in 1980.

DX 74108   DB 965318   74/033   457 1964
Allocated to the Stratford Division. Sold from Gidea Park to the Mid-Hants Railway 7/79. Resold to KESR 8/90.

DX 74109   DB 965258   74/034   445 1964
Allocated to the Stratford Division. Scrapped at Beighton by Ward, Sheffield 7/79.

DX 74110   DB 965259   74/035   446 1964
Allocated to the Leeds Division. Scrapped at Barlow RCE Tip by Hudson, Dudley 6/79.

DX 74111   DB 965260   74/036   447 1964
Allocated to the Doncaster Division. Scrapped at York Skelton by Ward, Sheffield 7/79.

DX 74112   DB 965261   74/037   448 1964
Allocated to the Stratford Division. Scrapped at Leyton by Hudson, Dudley 6/79.

DX 74113   –   PWM 5856   438 1964
Allocated to the Gloucester Division. Scrapped at Bristol Marsh Jn. by Cashmore, Newport 2/75.

DX 74114   –   PWM 5857   439 1964
Allocated to the Plymouth Division. To Eastern Region 1977. Scrapped at York Leeman Road by Berry, Leicester 1/79.

DX 74115   –   PWM 5858   440 1964
Initially allocated to the Plymouth Division. Later Newport Division. Finally Swansea Division. Scrapped at Danygraig by Cartwright, Tipton 12/77.

DX 74116   –   PWM 5859   441 1964
Allocated to the Taunton Division. Stripped at Westbourne Park and scrapped there by C & D Metals, Blackheath during 1975.

DX 74117   –   PWM 5860   442 1964
Initially allocated to the Bristol Division. Later Reading Division. To Gloucester Division 1974. To Preston Division 5/75. Later Watford Division. Scrapped at Rugby by Hudson, Dudley 11/79.

DX 74118   –   PWM 5861   450 1964
Allocated to the Newport Division. Scrapped at Cardiff Cathays by Cashmore, Newport 10/74.

DX 74119   –   PWM 5862   451 1964
Allocated to the Newport Division. Scrapped at Danygraig by Cooper, Swindon 7/75.

DX 74120   –   PWM 5863   452 1964
Allocated to the Bristol Division. To Manchester Division 12/75. Scrapped at Guide Bridge by Texas Metals, Hyde 11/78.

DX 74121   –   PWM 5864   454 1964
Allocated to the Gloucester Division. Stripped at Westbourne Park and scrapped there by a private contractor in 1975.

DX 74122   –   PWM 5865   459 1964
Allocated to the Swansea Division. Scrapped at Danygraig by Cooper, Swindon 7/75.

DX 74123   –   PWM 5866   460 1964
Allocated to the Swansea Division. Scrapped at Danygraig by Cooper, Swindon 7/75.

DX 74124   –   PWM 5869   449 1964
Allocated to the Western Region as a relief machine. Final allocation Taunton Division. Scrapped at Bristol Marsh Jn. by Cashmore, Newport 3/75.

DX 74125   –   PWM 5940   004 1965
Allocated to the Gloucester Division. Type MPT 195 a variation of the 05E. Scrapped at Bristol Marsh Jn. by Cashmore, Newport 10/74.

DX 74126   DB 965262   –   461 1964
Allocated to the Southern SW Division. Scrapped at Stewarts Lane by Claidon, Wandsworth 1/75.

DX 74127   DB 965263   –   462 1964
Allocated to the Southern Central Division. Later to Polegate for operator training. Broken up at Polegate by BR 3/76.

DX 74128   DB 965265   –   464 1964
Allocated to the Southern SE Division. Scrapped at Ashford by J & P Metals, St. Albans 3/76.

Plasser and Theurer VKR 06-16 Tamper

Vehicle no longer in stock:

DX 74200   –   PWM 6356   535 1966
Allocated to the Bristol Division. Scrapped at Bristol Marsh Jn. by Cooper, Swindon 7/75.

Plasser and Theurer 06-32 Duomatic Tamper

Vehicles no longer in stock:

DX 74300   DB 965395   DTM 66/1   554 1966
Initially allocated to the Scottish SE Division. Later Newcastle Division. Scrapped at Newcastle (Forth Goods) by Ward, Sheffield in 1978.

DX 74301   DB 965396   DTM 67/2   560 1966
Allocated to the Glasgow South Division. Scrapped at Kilmarnock RCE Workshops by Motherwell Scrap and Machinery 12/78.

DX 74302   DB 965397   DTM 67/3   586 1967
Allocated to the Scottish NE Division. Scrapped at Kilmarnock RCE Workshops by Motherwell Scrap and Machinery 12/78.

DX 74303   DB 965398   DTM 67/4   588 1967
Allocated to the Glasgow North Division. Scrapped at Shettleston by Hepburn, Coatbridge 5/78.

DX 74304   DB 965319   74/038   553 1966
Allocated to the Norwich Division. Broken up at Lowestoft Harbour Works in 1977.

DX 74305   DB 965320   74/040   585 1966
Initially allocated to the Doncaster Division. Later Leeds Division and then Kings Cross Division. Finally Newcastle Division. Scrapped at Newcastle (Forth Goods) by Newton, Durham 8/82.

DX 74306   DB 965321   74/041   587 1967
Allocated to the Kings Cross Division. Scrapped at Peterborough by Berry, Leicester in 1977.

DX 74307   DB 965322   74/042   589 1967
Allocated to the Sheffield Division. Scrapped at York Skelton by Ward, Sheffield 7/79.

DX 74308   DB 965305   74/044   596 1967
Allocated to the Newcastle Division. Scrapped at Newcastle (Forth Goods) by Newton, Durham 8/82.

DX 74309   DB 965306   74/045   598 1967
Allocated to the Newcastle Division. Scrapped at Durham by Newton, Durham during 1981.

DX 74310   DB 965539   DTM 8   599 1967
Allocated to the Birmingham Division. To Hitchin for stripping 5/78. Scrapped there by Ward, Sheffield 8/78.

DX 74311   DB 965541   DTM 1   590 1967
Allocated to the Watford Division. Scrapped at Rugby by Hudson, Derby 11/79.

DX 74312   DB 965542   DTM 2   591 1967
Initially allocated to the Nottingham Division. Transferred to York Division 1979. Scrapped at Barlow RCE Tip by Hampton, Keele 8/82.

DX 74313   DB 965543   DTM 3   592 1967
Initially allocated to the Crewe Division. Transferred to Sheffield Division 10/78. Scrapped at Barlow RCE Tip by Hampton, Keele 8/82.

DX 74314   DB 965544   DTM 4   593 1967
Initially allocated to the Manchester Division. Transferred to Stratford Division 11/78. Scrapped at Stratford by Cartwright, Tipton 7/83.

DX 74315   DB 965545   DTM 5   594 1967
Allocated to the Nottingham Division. Scrapped at Derby St. Mary's by Howard and Pepperell, Sheffield 2/81.

DX 74316   DB 965546   DTM 6   595 1967
Allocated to the Liverpool Division. Scrapped at Wavertree Road, Liverpool by Ward, Sheffield 2/82.

DX 74317   DB 965547   DTM 7   597 1967
Allocated to the Crewe Division. Sent to Hitchin for stripping but got no further than Rugby. Scrapped at Rugby by Cartwright, Tipton 6/79.

DX 74318   –   PWM 6380   559 1966
Allocated to the Bristol Division. Later Newport Division. Stripped at Westbourne Park and scrapped there by a private contractor 10/77.

DX 74319   DB 965294   –   555 1966
Allocated to the Southern SW Division. Sold to Ward, Ringwood for scrap and removed from site at Eastleigh 11/79.

DX 74320   DB 965295   –   556 1966
Allocated to the Southern Central Division. Scrapped at Three Bridges by Hudson, Dudley 7/79.

DX 74321   DB 965296   –   557 1966
Allocated to the Southern SE Division. To Hitchin for stripping 11/78. Scrapped at Hitchin by Round, Wednesbury 6/80.

DX 74322   DB 965297   –   558 1966
Allocated to the Southern SE Division. Scrapped at Ashford Old Loco Yard by Hudson, Dudley 7/79.

DX 74323   DB 965298   –   561 1966
Allocated to the Southern SW Division. Sold to Ward, Ringwood for scrap and removed from site at Eastleigh 11/79.

DX 74324   DB 965299   –   562 1966
Allocated to the Southern Central Division. To Hitchin for stripping 10/78. Scrapped at Hitchin by Round, Wednesbury 6/80.

Plasser and Theurer 06-32 Duomatic Tamper (Built by Rolls Royce, Shrewsbury)

Vehicles no longer in stock:

DX 74400   DB 965702   74/046   672 1968
Allocated to the Leeds Division. Damaged in an accident at Moorthorpe in 1982 and sold as scrap to Moorthorpe Saw Mill. Not yet scrapped.

DX 74401   DB 965714   74/047   684 1968
Allocated to the Doncaster Division. Scrapped at Durham by Newton, Durham 4/81.

DX 74402   DB 965717   74/048   687 1968
Allocated to the Doncaster Division. Scrapped at Peterborough by Cartwright, Tipton 5/83.

DX 74403   DB 965721   74/049   691 1968
Allocated to the York Division. Later Leeds Division. Scrapped at Barlow RCE Tip by Cartwright, Tipton 5/83.

DX 74404   DB 965540   DTM 9   600 1967
Allocated to the Preston Division. To Hitchin for stripping 9/78. Scrapped at Hitchin by Round, Wednesbury 9/79.

DX 74405   DB 965700   DTM 10   670 1968
Allocated to the Manchester Division. Scrapped at Guide Bridge by Texas Metals, Hyde 11/78.

DX 74406   DB 965701   DTM 11   671 1968
Allocated to the Preston Division.To Hitchin for stripping 10/78. Scrapped at Hitchin by Round Wednesbury 6/80.

DX 74407   DB 965703   DTM 12   673 1968
Allocated to the Nottingham Division. Retained at Derby Technical Centre for the track development section. Sold from Derby Technical Centre to Peak Rail, Darley Dale 8/90.

DX 74408   DB 965704   DTM 13   674 1968
Allocated to the Liverpool Division. Scrapped at Liverpool Wavertree Road by Ward, Sheffield 2/82.

DX 74409   DB 965706   DTM 14   676 1968
Allocated to the Birmingham Division. Scrapped at Tyseley by Bridges, Sutton Coldfield 2/82.

DX 74410   DB 965709   DTM 15   679 1968
Allocated to the Nottingham Division. Scrapped at Derby St. Mary's by Howard and Pepperell, Sheffield 2/81.

DX 74411   DB 965710   DTM 16   680 1968
Allocated to the Watford Division. Later Liverpool Division. Scrapped at Wavertree Road, Liverpool by Ward, Sheffield 2/82.

DX 74412   DB 965712   DTM 17   682 1968
Allocated to the Preston Division. Later Manchester Division. Scrapped at Stockport by Housley, Sheffield 2/81.

DX 74413   DB 965713   DTM 18   683 1968
Allocated to the Preston Division. Later Manchester Division. Scrapped at Stockport by Housley, Sheffield 2/81.

DX 74414   DB 965715   DTM 19   685 1968
Allocated to the Crewe Division. Later Nottingham Division. Scrapped at Derby St. Mary's by Howard and Pepperell, Sheffield 2/81.

DX 74415   DB 965716   DTM 20   686 1968
Allocated to the Manchester Division. To Hitchin for stripping 1/79. Scrapped at Hitchin by Round, Wednesbury 6/80.

DX 74416   DB 965718   DTM 21   688 1968
Initially allocated to the Crewe Division. Later Watford Division. Converted to Sleeper Squarer DX 94416 in 1983. Scrapped at Rugby by Cartwright, Bilston 9/85.

DX 74417   DB 965720   DTM 22   690 1968
Allocated to the Birmingham Division. To Hitchin for stripping 4/78. Scrapped there by Ward, Sheffield 8/78.

DX 74418   DB 965722   DTM 23   692 1968
Allocated to the Watford Division. Scrapped at Rugby by Berry, Leicester 2/81.

DX 74419   DB 965723   DTM 24   693 1968
Allocated to the Liverpool Division. Scrapped at Wavertree Road, Liverpool by Ward, Sheffield 2/82.

DX 74420   DB 965705   PWM 6533   675 1968
Initially allocated to the Reading Division. To Gloucester Division 7/74. Later Newport Division. To Bristol Division 1/77. To Hitchin for stripping 12/77. Scrapped there by Ward, Sheffield 8/78.

DX 74421   DB 965719   PWM 6592   689 1968
Allocated to the Newport Division. To Westbourne Park for stripping 1978. Scrapped at Westbourne Park by a private contractor in 1979.

DX 74422   DB 965707   –   677 1968
Allocated to the Southern SW Division. Scrapped at Basingstoke by British Contractors Plant, Staines 10/78.

DX 74423   DB 965708   –   678 1968
Allocated to the Southern Central Division. To Southern SE Division 1979. Scrapped at Hither Green by British Contractors Plant, Staines 1/80.

DX 74424   DB 965711   –   681 1968
Allocated to the Southern SE Division. Scrapped at Hither Green by British Contractors Plant, Staines 10/78.

Plasser and Theurer PLM 275 Switch and Crossing Tamper

Vehicles no longer in stock:

DX 74500   DB 965918   PS & CT 66/1   275 1966
Allocated to the Scottish Pool. Scrapped at Kilmarnock RCE Workshops by Burnett and Cairns, Dalkeith 3/80.

DX 74501   DB 965471   PS & CT 66/2   274 1966
Initially allocated to the London Midland Region. Transferred to the Scottish SE Division 9/71. Scrapped at Kilmarnock RCE Workshops by Berry, Leicester 12/77.

DX 74502   DB 965323   74/039   276 1966
Allocated to the Newcastle Squadron. Scrapped at Northallerton by Sheard, Wakefield 6/79.

DX 74503   DB 965302   74/043   278 1966
Allocated to the York Squadron. Loaned to Southern Region during 1974. Scrapped at Newcastle (Forth Goods) by a private contractor in 1977.

DX 74504   –   PWM 6086   236 1966
Allocated to the Bristol Division. Stripped at Westbourne Park and scrapped there by a private contractor 10/77.

DX 74505   DB 965301   PWM 6757   277 1966
Initially allocated to the Southern Region. To Gloucester Division 4/69. To Hitchin for stripping 6/78. Scrapped at Hitchin by Round, Wednesbury 9/79.

Plasser and Theurer Universal Joint Tamper

Vehicle no longer in stock:

DX 74600   DB 965359   74/080   U2053 1970
Allocated to the York Squadron. Scrapped at Barlow RCE Tip by Ward, Sheffield 11/79.

75XXX MID-RANGE TAMPERS/LINERS

The introduction in 1991 of three different types of machines (all of the mid-range type) has resulted in the second use of the 75XXX number series, that series having initially been used for lining machines, all of which have now been disposed of. Further orders are anticipated of mid-range machines once a period of evaluation and comparison has been completed. The first mid-range machine purchased by British Rail was DR 73501 a Plasser lightweight, single axle 08–16/90 tamping machine purchased in 1988. There is no immediate intention to renumber DR 73501 into this number series.

Plasser and Theurer 08–16/90 Tamper/Liner

Current Stock:

DR 75001   –   –   –   1991   Western Region

Tamper Mark III UIC Tamper/Liner

Current Stock:

DR 75101   –   –   S453   1991   Eastern Region

Plasser and Theurer 08–16/90–275 Switch and Crossing Tamper

Current Stock:

DR 75201   –   –   –   1991   Southern Region
DR 75202   –   –   –   1991   Southern Region

LINERS
(First use of 75XXX number series)

A vital aspect of routine track maintenance is keeping good alignment. Until 1965, this had always been done manually, the effectiveness depending very much on the ganger's ability to 'eye' in correctly. British Rail then purchased forty-one Automatic Lining machines from Plasser and Theurer. These machines (DX 750XX series) automatically measure the alignment, slew the track to improved alignment and record the actual curvature left behind. In 1970 these forty-one AL 203 Liners were supplemented by the purchase of eleven AL 250 Liners (DX 751XX series), these machines being able to line whilst rolling. The final purchase by British Rail of lining machines was of five Robel machines (DX 75200–4), the first arriving in 1972 and the other four in 1975.

The fifty seven machines in this section have all now been disposed of. As with the tampers in the 74XXX number series the combined lifting, levelling, tamping and lining machines (see 73XXX section) have of course accounted for the demise of these machines.

Plasser and Theurer AL 203 Liner

Vehicles no longer in stock:

DX 75000   DB 965399   PMTL 2D   207 1966
Allocated to the Glasgow South Division. Scrapped at Kilmarnock RCE Workshops by Motherwell Machinery and Scrap 12/78.

DX 75001   DB 965900   PMTL 3D   213 1966
Allocated to the Scottish Pool. Scrapped at Kilmarnock RCE Workshops by Hepburn, Coatbridge 11/78.

DX 75002   DB 965901   PMTL 4D   221 1966
Allocated to the Glasgow North Division. Scrapped at Kilmarnock RCE Workshops by a private contractor in 1982.

DX 75003   DB 965902   PMTL 5D   228 1966
Allocated to the Scottish SE Division. Scrapped at Kilmarnock RCE Workshops by Motherwell Machinery and Scrap in 1982.

DX 75004   DB 965903   PMTL 6D   235 1966
Allocated to the Scottish NE Division. Scrapped at Kilmarnock RCE Workshops by Motherwell Machinery and Scrap in 1982.

DX 75005   DB 965273   75/001   147 1965
Initially allocated to the Sheffield Division. Later Newcastle Division. Scrapped at Newcastle (Forth Goods) by Newton, Durham 9/82.

DX 75006   DB 965272   75/002   146 1965
Allocated to the Newcastle Division. Scrapped at Newcastle (Forth Goods) by Newton, Durham 8/82.

DX 75007   DB 965324   75/004   150 1965
Allocated to the Norwich Division. Later Newcastle Division. Scrapped at Newcastle (Forth Goods) by Cartwright, Tipton 6/83.

DX 75008   DB 965325   75/005   205 1966
Allocated to the Stratford Division. Scrapped at Hitchin by Cartwright, Tipton 6/83.

DX 75009   DB 965326   75/006   206 1966
Allocated to the Newcastle Division. Sold 12/82 from Newcastle (Forth Goods) to the Lower Swansea Railway Preservation Society, but subsequently scrapped at Newcastle (Forth Goods)1/85.

DX 75010   DB 965327   75/007   222 1966
Allocated to the Kings Cross Division. Sold 5/83 from Hitchin to the Dean Forest Railway Society but subsequently scrapped at Hitchin by Cartwright, Tipton 7/83.

DX 75011   DB 965328   75/008   233 1966
Allocated to the Leeds Division. Scrapped at Leeds Holbeck by Morley Waste Traders, Morley, Leeds 5/84.

DX 75012   DB 965329   75/009   312 1967
Allocated to the York Division. Scrapped at York Leeman Road by Morley Waste Traders, Morley, Leeds 5/84.

DX 75013   DB 965304   75/010   310 1967
Allocated to the Doncaster Division. Scrapped at Doncaster Marshgate by Wath Skip Hire 11/82.

DX 75014   DB 965430   PLM 30   229 1966
Allocated to the Watford Division. Broken up at Rugby by BR 4/83.

DX 75015   DB 965431   PLM 31   230 1966
Allocated to the Preston Division. Later Liverpool Division. Scrapped at Wavertree Road, Liverpool by Oldham Bros, Liverpool 12/82.

DX 75016   DB 965432   PLM 35   234 1966
Allocated to the Nottingham Division. Scrapped at Derby St. Mary's by Hill, Derby 1/83.

DX 75017   DB 965501   PLM 1   113 1964
Allocated to the Birmingham Division. To Hitchin for stripping 4/78. Scrapped at Hitchin by Stanley, Bexleyheath 3/79.

DX 75018   DB 965502   PLM 2   131 1965
Allocated to the Preston Division. Scrapped at Carnforth by Ward, Sheffield in 1980.

DX 75019   DB 965507   PLM 7   141 1965
Allocated to the Preston Division. Scrapped at Carlisle by Ward, Sheffield in 1980.

DX 75020   DB 965512   PLM 12   149 1965
Allocated to the Crewe Division. Scrapped at Cartwright, Tipton 2/82.

DX 75021   DB 965515   PLM 15   204 1966
Allocated to the Nottingham Division. To Hitchin 3/79. Transferred to the Scottish Region 1980/1. Allocated to the Glasgow South Division. Scrapped at Rutherglen by Henderson Kerr, Mossend 6/88.

DX 75022   DB 965521   PLM 21   220 1966
Allocated to the Manchester Division. Later shared with Liverpool Division for towing weedkilling equipment. Scrapped at Liverpool (Spekeland Road) by Oldham Bros., Liverpool 4/90.

DX 75023   DB 965527   PLM 27   226 1966
Allocated to the Liverpool Division. Scrapped at Wavertree Road, Liverpool by Ward, Sheffield 2/82.

DX 75024   DB 965528   PLM 41   314 1967
Allocated to the Watford Division. Scrapped at Rugby by Bridges, Sutton Coldfield 3/83.

DX 75025   −   PWM 5938   139 1965
Allocated to the Taunton Division. To Manchester Division 11/75. To Hitchin for stripping 3/79. Scrapped at Hitchin by Round, Wednesbury 9/79.

DX 75026   –   PWM 5939   140 1965
Allocated to the Newport Division. Stripped at Westbourne Park and scrapped there by a private contractor in 1975.

DX 75027   –   PWM 6074   212 1966
Allocated to the Reading Division. To Birmingham Division 11/75. To Hitchin for stripping 5/78. Scrapped at Hitchin by Stanley, Bexleyheath 3/79.

DX 75028   –   PWM 6085   211 1966
Allocated to the Bristol Division. To Watford Division 11/75. Scrapped at Rugby by Berry, Leicester 2/81.

DX 75029   –   PWM 6374   227 1966
Allocated to the Gloucester Division. Disposed of for scrap during the mid-1970s.

DX 75030   –   PWM 6381   224 1966
Allocated to the Swansea Division. Scrapped at Danygraig by Forester, Port Talbot 5/79.

DX 75031   –   PWM 6477   311 1967
Allocated to the Plymouth Division. To Westbourne Park for stripping 1978. Scrapped at Westbourne Park by a private contractor in 1979.

DX 75032   DB 965300   PWM 6661   225 1966
Initially allocated to the Eastern Region. Later Bristol Division. To Taunton Division 1976. To Westbourne Park for stripping 1978. Scrapped at Westbourne Park by a private contractor in 1979.

DX 75033   DB 965274   –   133 1965
Allocated to the Southern SW Division. Scrapped at Eastleigh PAD by Ward Ringwood 10/78.

DX 75034   DB 965930   –   135 1965
Initially allocated to the Scottish Region and originally incorrectly numbered DB 965250. To Southern SW Division 10/68. Scrapped at Eastleigh PAD by Ward, Sheffield 6/79.

DX 75035   DB 965275   –   143 1965
Allocated to the Southern Central Division. Scrapped at Sutton by C & D Metals, Blackheath 3/76.

DX 75036   DB 965276   –   144 1965
Allocated to the Southern SE Division. Later to Polegate for operator training. Believed broken up at Polegate by BR 2/77.

DX 75037   DB 965277   –   223 1966
Allocated to the Southern SW Division. Sold to Ward, Ringwood for scrap and removed from site at Eastleigh 11/79.

DX 75038   DB 965278   –   232 1966
Allocated to the Southern Central Division. Scrapped at Three Bridges by Bruce,Newham 5/78.

DX 75039   DB 965279   –   313 1967
Initially allocated to the Southern SE Division. To Hitchin 11/78. To Derby Technical Centre 1/79. Scrapped at York, Skelton by Hampton, Keele 7/83.

DX 75040   DB 965387   –   419 1971
Initially allocated to the Southern SE Division. To Sheffield Division 1979. Scrapped at Sheffield Darnall by Heselwood, Sheffield 5/84.

Plasser and Theurer AL 250 Liner

Vehicles no longer in stock:

DX 75100   DB 965354   75/011   414 1970
Initially allocated to the Doncaster Division. Transferred to Scottish NE Division 9/77. Scrapped at Kilmarnock RCE Workshops by Motherwell Machinery and Scrap in 1982.

DX 75101   DB 965476   PLM(A) 43   408 1970
Allocated to the Liverpool Division. Later Preston Division. Sold from Carnforth to the Mid-Hants Railway 2/83.

DX 75102   DB 965477   PLM(A) 44   409 1970
Allocated to the Birmingham Division. To Rugby in 1982 where it has been cut down to the frame and modified for use as a test bed for Rolls Royce engines and twin disc gearboxes. Still in use.

DX 75103   DB 965529   PLM(A) 45   411 1970
Allocated to the Crewe Division. Scrapped at Chester by Garrett, Crewe 3/83.

DX 75104   DB 965572   PLM(A) 42   320 1967
Allocated to the Manchester Division. Scrapped at Stockport by Housley, Sheffield 2/81.

DX 75105   –   PWM 7223   345 1970
Allocated to the Newport Division. To Westbourne Park for stripping 1979. Scrapped at Westbourne Park by Stanley, Bexleyheath 6/81.

DX 75106   –   PWM 7224   346 1970
Allocated to the Reading Division. To Doncaster Division. Believed scrapped at Barlow RCE Tip by Hampton, Keele 8/82.

DX 75107   –   PWM 7252   410 1970
Allocated to the Newport Division. Later Swansea Division. To Western RCE Training Centre at Westerleigh. Scrapped at Westerleigh by a private contractor 6/82.

DX 75108   DB 965340   –   349 1970
Allocated to the Southern SE Division. Scrapped at Hither Green by British Contractors Plant, Staines 2/82.

DX 75109   DB 965341   –   405 1970
Allocated to the Southern Central Division. Later Southern SW Division. Scrapped at Wimbledon by British Contractors Plant, Staines 2/82.

DX 75110   DB 965364   –   412 1970
Allocated to the Southern SW Division. Later Central Division. Scrapped at Three Bridges by Stanley, Bexleyheath 6/79.

Robel Liner

Vehicles no longer in stock:

DX 75200   DB 965927   75/012   24.21-53-RR2 1972
Allocated to the York HQ Section. Scrapped at York by Wakefield Metal Traders 2/80.

DX 75201   DB 966018   –   24.24-2-RV1 1975
Initially allocated to the Scottish Pool. Transferred to the York Squadron 9/77. To Doncaster Squadron 1979. Finally Doncaster Division. Offered for sale at Lincoln West Yard 1/84, but subsequently reserved for possible use by Derby Technical Centre. This use never materialised. Scrapped at Doncaster Marshgate by Bard Street Salvage, Parkgate, Rotherham 5/86.

DX 75202   DB 966019   –   24.24-2-RV2 1975
Initially allocated to the London Midland Region. Very soon transferred to the Bristol Division. Sold to Whitefield, Bratton (near Westbury) and removed from site at Bristol Marsh Jn. 11/82. Scrapped 11/83.

DX 75203   DB 966020   –   24.24-2-RV3 1975
Allocated to the Bristol Division. Sold to Whitefield, Bratton (near Westbury) and removed from site at Bristol Marsh Jn. 11/82. Scrapped 11/83.

DX 75204   DB 966021   –   24.24-2-RV4 1975
Allocated to the Southern Central Division. Scrapped at Earlswood by British Contractors Plant, Staines 5/82.

76XXX BALLAST CLEANERS

Before mechanisation ballast cleaning was confined to manual work in crib spaces and at shoulders. The under-sleeper material often contained very large stones from the original construction and which had been very rarely disturbed. So it had become very compacted and choked with steam locomotive ash and cinders. Research into the function of ballast showed that track is best supported by a resilient bed of ballast of definite gradation and at least nine inches depth. Tamping machines had also proved that hard sleeper beds could not be successfully tamped.

So it became essential to carry out complete ballast cleaning of all track, particularly that which was to be improved to new high speed standards. The object is to remove all ballast to at least nine inches below the base of the sleeper and then to riddle it and return the good stone that was within ballast specification size and then discard the remainder. The next stage is to reballast with new material to the desired specification.

The ballast cleaner is a large self-contained on-track unit which is self-propelled while it performs its task. From the machine two arms in the form of troughs slope downwards to position just outside the ends of the sleepers and to the predetermined depth below them. At this point the ballast is cut away beneath the track and another steel channel referred to as the cutting bar is inserted and bolted at each end to the sloping arms. This forms a triangular structure with its base at a fixed depth below the sleepers. An endless chain is fitted to run round the triangular troughing and connected to it are a series of projecting claws or cutters. When the chain is set in motion the ballast-cleaning machine moves forward. The wall of the old consolidated ballast facing the cutter bar is broken up and scraped away by the claws to be carried up one of the sloping troughs into the body of the machine. At the top of the trough the dirty ballast falls into a large bin and is vibrated over special screens or sieves. The clean ballast retained by the screens moves onwards to the rear end of the machine and is returned to the track, whereas the rejected small and dirty material falls onto a conveyor belt which disposes of it in waiting wagons or deposits along the lineside.

The first Ballast Cleaners purchased by British Rail were the Matisa 2 ST, none of which survived by the time the CEPS numbering scheme was originated. A fleet of larger Matisa Ballast Cleaners came between 1955-60 (DR 76000–18), followed by four larger machines in 1962 (DR 76100–3), whilst the final representatives of Matisa were the two C311 machines DR 76104/5. All the other machines are built by Plasser, DR 76200/1/6–8/11–4 being Series One, DR 76202–4/9/10 being Series Two, DR 76215/6 being Series Three and DR 76217–20 Series Four. The DR 76300 machines are Series Five.

The two Shoulder Ballast Cleaners DR 76400 and DR 76500 have both been disposed of. The introduction in 1991 of a new type of ballast cleaner has resulted in the second use of the 761XX series. The Kershaw High Output Ballast Cleaner DR 76101 is due to start a period of six months evaluation in the spring of 1991. DR 76101 is similar to current automatic ballast cleaners but uses a different, much faster method of operation and is quicker to start work on site.

As regards allocation, Ballast Cleaners generally work wherever required on their region, although for maintenance purposes they are allocated to the area listed.

Matisa 3B5 Ballast Cleaners

Vehicles no longer in stock:

DR 76000   –   MBC 1   105 1957
Allocated to the Scottish Pool. Scrapped at Kilmarnock RCE Workshops by Hepburn, Coatbridge 10/78.

DR 76001   DB 965147   MBC 3   116 1959
Originally allocated to the Eastern Region as 76/008. Later Scottish SE Division. Scrapped at Kilmarnock RCE Workshops by Burnett and Cairns, Dalkeith 3/80.

DR 76002   –   MBC 4   107 1957
Originally allocated to the Southern Region as DS 122. To Western Region 10/66 as PWM 6373. To Scottish Region 9/71. Allocated to the Pool. To Horwich for spares 1978. To Leamington Spa for storage 7/79. Scrapped at Roberts, Stanton Gate 5/80.

DR 76003   DB 965040   76/001   101 1955
Allocated to the Eastern Region. Damaged in an accident at Low Fell 1975. Taken to Lowestoft for stripping for spares. Acquired internal User No. 041398. Scrapped at Lowestoft by Webster, Dinnington 6/82.

DR 76004   DB 965122   76/002   102 1955
Allocated to the Eastern Region. Stored at Peterborough from 1980. Scrapped at King, Snailwell 6/82.

DR 76005   DB 965024   76/004   109 1957
Allocated to the Eastern Region. Stored at Hitchin from 1980. Scrapped At King, Snailwell 6/82.

DR 76006   DB 965023   76/005   108 1957
Allocated to the Eastern Region. Stored at Lowestoft from 1980. Scrapped at King, Snailwell 6/82.

DR 76007   DB 965145   76/006   114 1958
Allocated to the Eastern Region. Stored at York Warehouse Yard from 1979. Scrapped at Howard and Pepperell, Sheffield 1/81.

DR 76008   DB 965146   76/007   115 1959
Allocated to the Eastern Region. Stored at York Warehouse Yard from 1979. Scrapped at Howard and Pepperell, Sheffield 1/81.

DR 76009   –   76/015   106 1957
Originally allocated to the Southern Region as DS 120. To Western Region 10/66 as PWM 6372. To Eastern Region 1/72. Stored at Lowestoft from 1980. Scrapped at King, Snailwell 6/82.

DR 76010   DB 965530   BC 30   103 1955
Allocated to the London Midland Region. To Leamington Spa for storage 7/79. Scrapped at Roberts, Stanton Gate 6/80.

DR 76011   DB 965531   BC 31   111 1957
Allocated to the London Midland Region. To Leamington Spa for storage 7/79. Scrapped at Roberts, Stanton Gate 6/80.

DR 76012   DB 965532   BC 32   112 1958
Allocated to the London Midland Region. To Leamington Spa for storage 7/79. Scrapped at Roberts, Stanton Gate 5/80.

DR 76013   DB 965533   BC 33   113 1958
Allocated to the London Midland Region. To Leamington Spa for storage 7/79. Scrapped at Roberts, Stanton Gate 6/80.

DR 76014   DB 965535   BC 35   118 1960
Allocated to the London Midland Region. To Leamington Spa for storage 7/79. Scrapped at Roberts, Stanton Gate 5/80.

DR 76015   –   PWM 4244   104 1956
Allocated to the Western Region. Scrapped at Cardiff Cathays by Knill, Barry 7/79.

DR 76016   DB 965534   PWM 7559   117 1960
Initially allocated to the London Midland Region as BC 34. To Western Region 1972. Scrapped at Swindon RCE Stores by Round, Wednesbury 1/80.

DR 76017   DB 965536   PWM 7560   119 1960
Initially allocated to the London Midland Region as BC 36. To Western Region 1972. Scrapped at Swindon RCE Stores by Round, Wednesbury 1/80.

DR 76018   DB 965159   76/003   110 1957
Initially allocated to the Eastern Region. To Western Region 1/73 becoming PWM 7625. To London Midland Region 9/74. To Leamington Spa for storage 7/79. Scrapped at Roberts, Stanton Gate 6/80.

Kershaw High Output Ballast Cleaner

Current Stock:

DR 76101   –   –   – 1991 London Midland Region

Matisa 8CB5 Ballast Cleaner
(First use of 761XX number series)

Vehicles no longer in stock:

DR 76100   DB 965181   76/009   2514 1961
Allocated to the Eastern Region. Stored at Lowestoft from 1980. Scrapped at King, Snailwell 6/82.

DR 76101   DB 965182   76/010   2515 1961
Allocated to the Eastern Region. Stored at Lowestoft from 1980. Scrapped at King, Snailwell 6/82.

DR 76102   DB 965188   PWM 7609   2546 1962
Initially allocated to the Scottish Region as MBC 2. To Western Region 11/72. To Eastern Region 1980. Scrapped at March by Cartwright, Tipton 5/83.

DR 76103   DB 965193   BC 3   2578 1962
Allocated to the Southern Region. Scrapped at New Cross Gate by Stanley, Bexleyheath 9/80.

Matisa C311 Ballast Cleaner
(First use of 761XX number series)

Current Stock:

DR 76104   DB 966016   –   2654 1975   Kilmarnock OOU

DR 76105   DB 966017   –   2655 1975   Kilmarnock OOU

Note: The power unit sections of DR 76104/5 have been removed and converted into RCE Depot shunters 97603/1 respectively.

Plasser and Theurer RM 62 Ballast Cleaner

Current Stock:

DR 76200   DB 965388   PBC 66/1   12 1966   Rutherglen OOU
DR 76201   DB 965389   PBC 66/2   16 1966   Glasgow
DR 76202   DB 965390   PBC 71/3   55 1970   Scottish SE

DR 76203	DB 965360	76/013	53 1970	Stratford
DR 76204	DB 965361	76/014	56 1970	Stratford

DR 76205 – believed reserved in error for BC 36 (DR 76017)

DR 76206	DB 965537	BC 37	15 1966	Llandudno Jn. OOU
DR 76207	DB 965538	BC 38	19 1966	Nottingham Eastcroft OOU
DR 76208	–	PWM 6360	14 1966	Glasgow
DR 76209	–	PWM 7243	54 1970	Leeds
DR 76210	–	PWM 7244	57 1970	South Wales
DR 76211	DB 965280	BC 4	11 1966	Rugby OOU
DR 76213	DB 965282	BC 6	17 1966	Southern SE
DR 76214	DB 965283	BC 7	18 1966	Derby Technical Centre
DR 76215	DB 965984	PWM 8052	72 1973	Reading
DR 76216	DB 965985	BC 39	73 1973	Watford
DR 76217	DB 966012	–	88 1974	Nottingham
DR 76218	DB 966013	–	89 1974	Bristol
DR 76219	DB 966014	–	90 1974	Crewe
DR 76220	DB 966015	–	91 1974	Scottish SE

Vehicle no longer in stock:

DR 76212	DB 965281	BC 5	13 1966	

Allocated to the Southern Region. To Eastern Region 1982. To Scottish Region 1985. Converted in 1986 at Kilmarnock RCE Workshops to RCE Depot Shunter 97602.

Plasser and Theurer RM 74 Ballast Cleaner

Current Stock:

DR 76300	–	–	140 1978	Glasgow
DR 76301	–	–	141 1978	Scottish NE
DR 76303	–	–	143 1978	Southern SE
DR 76304	–	–	144 1978	Nottingham
DR 76305	–	–	145 1978	Newcastle
DR 76306	–	–	146 1978	Newcastle
DR 76307	–	–	147 1979	Reading
DR 76308	–	–	148 1978	South Wales
DR 76309	–	–	149 1979	Manchester
DR 76310	–	–	150 1979	Watford
DR 76311	–	–	151 1979	Stratford
DR 76312	–	–	152 1979	Leeds
DR 76313	–	–	153 1979	Bristol
DR 76314	–	–	154 1979	Preston
DR 76315	–	–	155 1979	Birmingham
DR 76316	–	–	169 1979	Exeter
DR 76317	–	–	170 1979	Southern SE
DR 76318	–	–	171 1979	Leeds
DR 76319	–	–	172 1979	Stratford
DR 76320	–	–	173 1979	Leeds
DR 76321	–	–	225 1983	Birmingham
DR 76322	–	–	229 1983	South Wales

Vehicle no longer in stock:

DR 76302	–	–	142 1978	

Allocated to the London Midland Region. Badly damaged by fire at Cricklewood on 07/05/89. Scrapped at Nottingham Eastcroft by Howard and Wheeler, Ecclesfield 6/90.

Hunslet Shoulder Ballast Cleaner

Vehicle no longer in stock:

DR 76400   DB 965169 76/011   5617 1961
Allocated to the Eastern Region. Scrapped at York Skelton by Berry, Leicester in 1978.

Plasser and Theurer SV 52 Shoulder Ballast Cleaner

Vehicle no longer in stock:

DR76500   DB 965561 76/012   22 1961
Initially allocated to the London Midland Region. Transferred to the Eastern Region 1970. Believed scrapped at South Pelaw by Berry, Leicester in 1978.

77XXX BALLAST REGULATORS

These are basically simple machines, similar to highway grading equipment with adjustable ploughs for working in the gaugeway of the track and the area between the adjacent tracks. A rotating brush feeding a transverse conveyor completes the rather coarse ploughing operation and disposes of surplus ballast to left or right – or to a storage hopper on the machine, by means of which the surplus or recovered ballast can be transported for a considerable distance and deposited. The purpose of these machines is to place the ballast in the sleeper cribs for tamping and to sweep and tidy the track after tamping.

The first ballast regulators were the Plasser USP 3000C which had shoulder and crown ploughs, a sweeper unit and a storage wagon and the Matisa R7 DX 77100 and R7D DX 77101–9. All these early ballast regulators have now been disposed of. The trend towards producing track maintenance machines in standard railway design led to the construction of the USP 4000C and later the USP 5000C. The latter machine has bogies, a sturdy frame as well as buffer and drawgear at each end of the machine and two cabins. DR 77300–3 are Series one, DR 77304–11 are Series two, DR 77312 is Series three, DR 77313–5 are Series four, DR 77316 is Series five, DR 77317–25 are Series six, DR 77326–30 are Series seven, DR 77331–4 are Series eight and DR 77335/6 are Series nine. DR 77400–3 were built by Cowans Sheldon at Carlisle

The introduction in 1991 of three mid-range ballast regulators, each from a different manufacturer, has resulted in the introduction of the 775XX, 776XX and 777XX series of numbers.

Plasser and Theurer USP 3000C Ballast Regulator

Vehicles no longer in stock:

DX 77000   DB 965909   PBR 68/1   34 1968
Allocated to the Glasgow North Division. Scrapped at Kilmarnock RCE Workshops by Nene Mechanical Handling, Northampton 9/84.

DX 77001   DB 965910   PBR 71/1   118 1970
Allocated to the Glasgow South Division. Badly damaged by fire at Cleland and scrapped at Kilmarnock RCE Workshops by Motherwell Scrap and Machinery 6/81.

DX 77002   DB 965911   PBR 71/3   117 1970
Allocated to the Scottish SE Division. Scrapped at Kilmarnock RCE Workshops by Hepburn, Coatbridge 5/88.

DX 77003   DB 965339   77/001   107 1969
Allocated to the Norwich Division. Scrapped at Lowestoft by Miller, Downham Market 4/84.

DX 77004   DB 965349   77/002   116 1970
Allocated to the Stratford Division. Scrapped at Hitchin by Berry, Leicester 5/86.

DX 77005   DB 965475   RB3   115 1970
Allocated to the Liverpool Division. Later Preston Division. Scrapped at Carnforth by Rollason, Telford 4/88.

DX 77006   DB 965480   RB1   103 1969
Allocated to the Birmingham Division. Later Watford Division. Scrapped at Rugby by Rollason, Telford 4/88.

DX 77007   –   PWM 7255   114 1970
Initially allocated to the Reading Division. Later Exeter Division. Scrapped at Plymouth Tavistock Jn. by Plant Dismantlers, Plymouth 11/84.

Matisa R7D Ballast Regulator

Vehicles no longer in stock:

DX 77100   DB 965394   MB 68/1   618 1968
Allocated to the Scottish NE Division. Later Scottish Pool. Finally Glasgow North Division. Scrapped at Kilmarnock RCE Workshops by Hepburn, Coatbridge 5/88.

DX 77101   DB 965355   77/003   6239 1971
Allocated to the York Squadron. Later York Regional HQ and finally Newcastle Division. Used in 1983 by BR as a source of spare parts and scrapped by Matisa at Bedford.

DX 77102   DB 965383   77/004   6274 1972
(with hopper DB 965924)
Allocated to the York Division. Damaged in an accident at York Skelton in 1981 and broken up there by British Rail 7/83.

DX 77103   DB 965382   77/005   6275 1972
(with hopper DB 965923)
Allocated to the Leeds Division. Badly damaged in an accident at Oakenshaw in 1976. Remains disposed of from York Leeman Road 1976.

DX 77104   DB 965385   77/006   6276 1972
(with hopper DB 965926)
Allocated to the Sheffield Division. Later York Division. Finally Leeds Division. Scrapped at Wakefield Kirkgate by Maize Metals, West Bromwich 4/87.

DX 77105   DB 965384   RB 5   6273 1972
(with hopper DB 965925)
Allocated to the Crewe Division. Broken up at Crewe Gresty Road by BR 5/86.

DX 77106   DB 965474   RB 2   6226 1970
Allocated to the Nottingham Division. Sold from Derby Etches Park to the Kent and East Sussex Railway 9/87.

DX 77107   DB 965485   RB 4   6238 1971
Allocated to the Preston Division. Scrapped at Preston Lostock Hall by Texas Metals, Hyde 3/85.

DX 77108   –   PWM 7253   6227 1970
Allocated to the Bristol Division. Scrapped at Bristol Marsh Junction by Whitefield, Bratton (near Westbury) 8/83.

DX 77109   –   PWM 7254   6240 1971
Initially allocated to the Newport Division. To Swansea Division 1976. Badly damaged by fire at Danygraig on 20/10/80. Remains removed by British Rail 3/81.

DX 77100   DB 965394   MB 68/1   6181 1968
Allocated to the Scottish NE Division. Later Scottish Pool. Finally Glasgow North Division. Scrapped at Kilmarnock RCE Workshops by Hepburn, Coatbridge 5/88.

DX 77101   DB 965355   77/003   6239 1971
Allocated to the York Squadron. Later York Regional HQ and finally Newcastle Division. Used in 1983 by BR as a source of spare parts and scrapped by Matisa at Bedford.

DX 77102   DB 965383   77/004   6274 1972
(with hopper DB 965924)
Allocated to the York Division. Damaged in an accident at York Skelton in 1981 and broken up there by British Rail 7/83.

DX 77103   DB 965382   77/005   6275 1972
(with hopper DB 965923)
Allocated to the Leeds Division. Badly damaged in an accident at Oakenshaw in 1976. Remains disposed of from York Leeman Road 1976.

DX 77104   DB 965385   77/006   6276 1972
(with hopper DB 965926)
Allocated to the Sheffield Division. Later York Division. Finally Leeds Division. Scrapped at Wakefield Kirkgate by Maize Metals, West Bromwich 4/87.

DX 77105   DB 965384   RB 5   6273 1972
(with hopper DB 965925)
Allocated to the Crewe Division. Broken up at Crewe Gresty Road by BR 5/86.

DX 77106   DB 965474   RB 2   6226 1970
Allocated to the Nottingham Division. Sold from Derby Etches Park to the Kent and East Sussex Railway 9/87.

DX 77107   DB 965485   RB 4   6238 1971
Allocated to the Preston Division. Scrapped at Preston Lostock Hall by Texas Metals, Hyde 3/85.

DX 77108   –   PWM 7253   6227 1970
Allocated to the Bristol Division. Scrapped at Bristol Marsh Junction by Whitefield, Bratton (near Westbury) 8/83.

DX 77109   –   PWM 7254   6240 1971
Initially allocated to the Newport Division. To Swansea Division 1976. Badly damaged by fire at Danygraig on 20/10/80. Remains removed by British Rail 3/81.

Plasser and Theurer USP 4000C Ballast Regulator

Current Stock:

DR 77201	DB 965573	RB 6	168 1973	Watford

Vehicles no longer in stock:

DR 77200	DB 965959	77/007	167 1973	

Allocated to the Doncaster Division. Scrapped at Doncaster Marshgate by Housley, Sheffield 4/85.

DR 77202	DB 965958	PWM 7729	166 1973	

Allocated to the Taunton Division. Later Exeter Division. Scrapped at Truro by Rollason, Telford 8/89.

Plasser and Theurer USP 5000C Ballast Regulator

Current Stock:

DR 77300	DB 965980	77/008	202 1974	York Leeman Road OOU
DR 77301	DB 965981	–	203 1974	Scottish NE
DR 77302	DB 965982	RB 7	204 1974	Manchester
DR 77303	DB 965983	–	205 1974	Scottish NE
DR 77304	DB 966004	–	243 1974	Slateford OOU
DR 77305	DB 966005	–	244 1974	Peterborough
DR 77306	DB 966006	RB 8	245 1974	Crewe
DR 77307	DB 966007	–	246 1974	Bristol
DR 77308	DB 966008	–	247 1974	Peterborough
DR 77309	DB 966009	RB 9	248 1974	Birmingham
DR 77310	DB 966010	–	249 1974	South Wales
DR 77311	DB 966011	–	250 1974	Bristol
DR 77312	–	–	340 1979	South Wales
DR 77313	–	–	361 1981	Newcastle
DR 77314	–	–	362 1981	Glasgow
DR 77315	–	–	363 1981	Southern SW
DR 77316	–	–	372 1981	Southern SE
DR 77317	–	–	376 1982	Leeds
DR 77318	–	–	377 1982	Newcastle
DR 77319	–	–	378 1983	Norwich
DR 77320	–	–	379 1983	Nottingham
DR 77321	–	–	380 1983	Merseyside
DR 77322	–	–	381 1983	Stratford
DR 77323	–	–	382 1983	Doncaster
DR 77324	–	–	383 1983	Exeter
DR 77325	–	–	384 1983	Exeter
DR 77326	–	–	389 1983	Leeds
DR 77327	–	–	390 1983	Crewe
DR 77328	–	–	391 1983	Preston
DR 77329	–	–	392 1984	Scottish SE
DR 77330	–	–	393 1984	Glasgow
DR 77331	–	–	400 1984	Glasgow
DR 77332	–	–	401 1984	Reading
DR 77333	–	–	402 1984	Doncaster
DR 77334	–	–	403 1984	Kilmarnock OOU
DR 77335	–	–	409 1985	Preston
DR 77336	–	–	410 1985	Southern Central

Cowans Sheldon Ballast Regulator

Current Stock:

DR 77400	–	–	34669 1984	Preston
DR 77401	–	–	34670 1984	Watford
DR 77402	–	–	34671 1984	Nottingham
DR 77403	–	–	34672 1984	Birmingham

The few surviving Plasser Rail Profilers are all stored awaiting either disposal or conversion. This photograph shows DR 79104 stabled in the sidings at the west end of Newport station on 19th February 1988.

Deryck W. Lewis

Kershaw 66–3 Ballast Regulator

Current Stock:

DR 77501	–	–	108 1990	Reading

Permaquip Ballast Regulator

Current Stock:

DR 77601	–	–	– 1991	Leeds or Peterborough

Plasser SSP 500 Ballast Regulator

Current Stock:

DR 77701	–	–	536 1990	Leeds or Peterborough

79XXX MISCELLANEOUS TRACK MACHINES

This number range is used for track machines on trial, evaluation, hire etc. and which cannot be conveniently numbered in the main series of machines.

DX 79001 was originally a Plasser Rail Changer, but in 1987 it was converted to a RAMM (Rail and Material Mover).

DX 79101–5 are Plasser Rail Profilers and are permanently coupled with a swarf collection unit. DX 79101's swarf collection unit was initially given its own number of 79102. However this number was dropped as the swarf wagon is permanently coupled to the Rail Profiler. Thus DX 79102 became DX 79101A. These machines reprofile used rails in-situ. Unlike rail grinding, reprofiling uses cutting tools, similar to those in machine tools, to cut thin layers of metal off the railhead and restore the correct profile. The cuts are made as the machine travels along the track. DX 79101 has been disposed of whilst DX 79102–5 are all stored awaiting either further conversion or disposal.

The DX 792XX series is for Speno Rail Grinding Trains which are hired by British Rail. Fitted with grindstones which can be adjusted to any angle, the trains automatically reprofile rails and smooth out corrugations and pitmarks. Two new trains were introduced in 1990 to replace DR 79200–14. DR 79215–20, DR 79221–6 are Type RPS 32–1 and RPS 32–2 respectively.

DX 79300 the Donelli Sleeper Spacer and Rail Positioner was used in conjunction with sleeper beam track renewals, whilst DR 79400/1 are Rail Grinders for working with Plasser Rail Joint Straighteners DR 86100/1. DX 79500 was a URR 16P compact grinder which packs 16 grinding stones into a 26 t unit. It was intended for grinding points and crossings. However the grindstones have now been removed and replaced by wire brushes for removing leaves from the track.

Plasser and Theurer RCM 100 Rail Changer

Vehicle no longer in stock:

DX 79001	–	–	8948 1979	

Converted at Kilmarnock RCE Workshops to a Rail and Material Mover in 1987. See DX 98402.

Plasser and Theurer RPM 100 Rail Profiler and SBM 110 Swarf Wagon

Current Stock:

DX 79102	–	–	31 1982	York Leeman Road OOU
DX 79102A	–	–	No separate identification	
DX 79103	–	–	32 1982	Nottingham Eastcroft OOU
DX 79103A	–	–	No separate identification	
DX 79104	–	–	33 1982	Gloucester OOU
DX 79104A	–	–	No separate identification	
DX 79105	–	–	34 1982	Kilmarnock OOU
DX 79105A	–	–	No separate identification	

Vehicle no longer in stock:

DX 79101	–	–	22 1979	

(with swarf wagon DX 79101A which had a separate works number 24 1979). Allocated to York Regional HQ. Scrapped at York Leeman Road by Howard and Wheeler, Ecclesfield 12/88.

Speno Rail Grinding Train

Current Stock:

(1)

DR 79215	–	–	–	1989	Locomotive
DR 79216	–	–	–	1989	Workshop
DR 79217	–	–	–	1989	Workshop
DR 79218	–	–	–	1989	Stores
DR 79219	–	–	–	1989	Stores
DR 79220	–	–	–	1989	Staff and Dormitory

Note: DX 79215–20 left BR in 1/91 and are currently working in France.

(2)

DR 79221	–	–	1990	Locomotive
DR 79222	–	–	1990	Workshop
DR 79223	–	–	1990	Workshop
DR 79224	–	–	1990	Stores
DR 79225	–	–	1990	Stores
DR 79226	–	–	1990	Staff and Dormitory

Vehicles no longer in stock:

DX 79200–5   –   –   1246 1980

(Locomotive/Stores/Stores/Generator and Workshop/Staff and Dormitory/Control Trailer).
Set 555A was allocated for working on the Eastern, Western and Scottish Regions. This train was returned to Speno, Geneva, Switzerland at the end of its hire contract 6/89.

DX 79206–10   –   –   1245 1980

(Locomotive/Stores/Generator and Workshop/Staff and Dormitory/Control Trailer).
Set 555B was allocated for working on the London Midland Region. Sent to Marple and Gillott, Sheffield 6/89, DX 79206–9 being scrapped 6/90 and DX 79210 7/90.

DX 79211–4   –   –   2530 1985

(Locomotive/Generator and Workshop/Staff and Dormitory/Control Trailer).
Allocated to the Southern Region. This URR48–4 train was returned to Speno, Geneva, Switzerland at the end of its five year hire contract 10/89.

Donelli Sleeper Spacer and Rail Positioner

Vehicle no longer in stock

DX 79300   –   –   600185 1983
Allocated to the Eastern Region. Resold to Donelli and returned to Italy 7/87.

Plasser and Theurer GWM 110 Rail Grinder

Current Stock:

DX 79400	–	–	2147 1984	Crewe Gresty Road OOU
DX 79401	–	–	38 1985	Southern Region

Speno URR 16P Rail Grinder

Current Stock:

DX 79500	–	–	1991 1983	Southern Region

Note: Currently in use for leaf removal from rails.

TRACK RELAYERS/
BALLAST PROFILERS

The earliest machines (780XX) were designed for lifting timber sleepered track and had a maximum lift of 6t. They had two towers, each fitted with a manually extended jib and a compressed air winch powered each hoist rope. This equipment was mounted on Warwell wagons, whilst a second vehicle carried two mobile compressors and a large air receiver.

Also numbered in the 780XX series because they had the same lifting capacity were 78000/7, these two machines being designed by the RM & EE, WR. They had no traction, but had manual slewing, hydraulic powered hoist and a fixed length jib. A central cab had full controls at each side of the machine. This type of machine was later upgraded to 10t, five being built – 78100/4/14–6.

The 781XX category of track-relayers is for non-self propelled vehicles. 78110/1 were Cowans Sheldon three jib cranes whilst 78101–3/6–9/12/3/19–23 are Warwell wagons with two British Hoist and Crane 6 t mobile cranes mounted on them. 78117/8 were Coles cranes mounted on Warwell wagons whilst 78105 was similar to 78100/4/14–6 but was built by Taylor and Hubbard. They then built two basically similar machines (78200/1) with a capacity of 11.4t and powered in all motions. Travel speed was 6 mph and nine similar machines (78202–10) were acquired from Thomas Smith.

A new specification was produced in 1975 for a heavier duty track relayer to lift out existing track and replace it with new prefabricated sections while working from an adjacent line. They were to be able to lift heavy track panels of up to thirty concrete sleepers. Plasser supplied 78211–24 whilst Cowans Sheldon supplied 78225–38. Although each type of crane was built to the same general specifications, each manufacturer was able to develop his own designs within the framework laid down. Two separate lifting units are mounted on a steel underframe, both units being controlled from a centrally-mounted operators cab. Although the lifting capacity is 12.5 t overall, each individual lifting unit is rated at 7 t to cater for any unequal lift of track panels. The crane jibs stow within the carriage length when not in use, pointing inwards towards the operator's cab.

The disadvantage of this type of track relayer is that possession of two tracks is required, whilst of course the machines cannot be used on single lines. The 783XX single line track relayers were therefore acquired and have given much valuable experience in single line occupation tracklaying. They are of the Goliath crane type, with four telescoping legs and hydraulically powered in all motions. The four wheels run on service rails laid temporarily on each side of the track. Two gantries, independently operated, work as a team taking out old track panels and laying in new panels. The later machines were joined by a long beam with power operated clips so that new concrete sleepers could be laid in directly.

The next range of single line track relayers was the Donelli PD350 (784XX), these replacing the 783XX series. Initially 78400/1 were numbered 78346/7. Since 1987 78404/5/10/1/6/7/20–3/6/7 have been modified and renovated. This work has included full hydraulic control, improved traction and braking, plus other modifications designed to bring the gantries up to the latest standards and to extend their working life. As regards allocation track relayers generally work wherever required on their region, although for maintenance purposes they are allocated to the area listed.

In 1986 this group of plant numbers was extended to include the Bruff Ballast Profilers 78501–5. These machines grade/profile/compact ballast in single or multiple loose sleeper relaying working and enable line opening speeds of 50 mph instead of 20 mph. The initial development was undertaken by the Scottish Region who used a Zet-Cat fitted with an adjustable profiling blade and vibrating plate compactors, forming a unit that could be transported on a wagon and was small enough to work under single-track relaying gantries. The prototype is numbered 08000.

A rationalisation of track relayers has taken place and only two 781XX machines remain in service, although four others survive out of use and awaiting disposal. Seven of the early series of 782XX self-propelled track-relayers survive including two which are out of use awaiting disposal.

British Rail Light Duty Non Self Propelled Twin Jib Crane

Vehicles no longer in stock:

DRB 78000   DB 965312   TRM 2/6   –   1956
Allocated to the Scottish Pool. Scrapped at Cohen, Motherwell 5/81.

DRB 78001   DM 748325   78/001   –   1950
Allocated to the Eastern Region. Scrapped at Wath, by Webster, Dinnington 2/81.

DRB 78002   DM 721283   78/003   –   1954
Allocated to the Eastern Region. Scrapped at Beighton by Howard and Pepperell, Sheffield 2/81.

DRB 78003   DE 314145   78/004   –   1954
Allocated to the Eastern Region. Scrapped at Beighton by Cartwright, Tipton 2/81.

DRB 78004   DB 965401   TRM 1   –   1951
Allocated to the London Midland Region. Scrapped at Newton Heath RCE Depot by Berry, Leicester 11/77.

DRB 78005   DB 965402   TRM 2   –   1951
Allocated to the London Midland Region. Scrapped at Newton Heath RCE Depot by Seddon, Webby & Co, Sale during 1976.

DRB 78006   DB 965403   TRM 3   –   1951
Allocated to the London Midland Region. Scrapped at Newton Heath RCE Depot by Corbard Contractors 2/81.

DRB 78007   –   DW 215   –   1948
£ Allocated to the Western Region. Scrapped at Bristol East by Knill, Barry 11/81.

DRB 78008   DS 82   TRU 1   –   1948
Allocated to the Southern Region. Scrapped by Smeeth Metal at Hoo Jn. 8/76.

DRB 78009   DS 84   TRU 3   –   1951
Allocated to the Southern Region. Scrapped by Smeeth Metal at Wimbledon 2/82, except for the wagon on which the cranes were mounted, that being broken up at Ashford Works 4/82.

DRB 78010   DS 87   TRU 4   –   1954
Allocated to the Southern Region. Scrapped by Smeeth Metal at Wimbledon 2/82, except for the wagon on which the cranes were mounted, that being broken up at Ashford Works 4/82.

DRB 78011   DS 70001   TRU 5   –   1957
Allocated to the Southern Region. Scrapped by Smeeth Metal at Wimbledon 2/82, except for the wagon on which the cranes were mounted, that being broken up at Ashford Works 4/82.

Heavy Duty Non-Self-Propelled Twin Jib Crane

Current Stock:

DRT 78105	DB 965187	78/007	1756 1962	York Leeman Road OOU
DRB 78109	DM 748303	78/017	– 1971	York Leeman Road OOU
DRB 78112	DM 748306	TRM 13	– 1970	Rugby OOU
DRB 78113	DM 748317	TRM 14	– 1970	Birmingham
DRB 78121	DB 966022	TRM 15	– 1975	Spekeland Road Goods Yard OOU
DRB 78123	DB 966024	TRM 17	– 1975	Glasgow

Vehicles no longer in stock:

DRB 78100   DB 965311   TRM 1/10   1953
Allocated to the Scottish Pool. Scrapped at Mossend by Hepburn, Coatbridge 3/82.

DRB 78101   DM 748301   TRM 3/12   –   1971
Allocated to the Scottish Pool. Sold from Kilmarnock and scrapped at R & M Supplies, Inverkeithing 7/88.

DRB 78102   DM 748344   TRM 4/12   –   1971
Allocated to the Scottish Pool. Scrapped at Rutherglen by Henderson Kerr, Mossend 6/88.

DRB 78103   DM 748321   TRM 5/12   –   1971
Allocated to the Scottish Pool. Scrapped at Perth by Mountelm, Carlisle 3/90.

DRB 78104   DB 966480   78/002   –   1952
Allocated to the Eastern Region. Sold from York and scrapped at Thompson, Stockton 7/82.

DRB 78106   DM 748311   78/014   –   1970
Allocated to the Eastern Region. Broken up at Shildon Works 11/83.

DRB 78107   DM 748339   78/015   –   1971
Allocated to the Eastern Region. Scrapped at Doncaster Wood Yard by Howard and Wheeler, Ecclesfield 8/90.

DRB 78108   DM 748337   78/016   –   1971
Allocated to the Eastern Region. Scrapped at Doncaster Wood Yard by Howard and Wheeler, Ecclesfield 7/90.

DRC 78110   DB 965404   TRM 4   74 1960
Allocated to the London Midland Region. Scrapped at Rugby by Cartwright, Tipton 3/83.

DRC 78111   DB 965405   TRM 5   75 1960
Allocated to the London Midland Region. Scrapped at Rugby by Cartwright, Tipton 3/83.

DRB 78114   –   DW 274   –   1953
Allocated to the Western Region. Scrapped at Hereford by Cashmore, Great Bridge 2/83.

DRB 78115   –   DW 275   –   1953
Allocated to the Western Region. Scrapped at Swindon Brickyard by Roth, Luton 3/82.

DRB 78116   –   DW 276   –   1953
Initially allocated to the Western Region. To Scottish Region 1/79. Scrapped at Mossend by Motherwell Scrap and Machinery in 1982.

, 3 78117   DM 721234   TRU 6   –   1962
Allocated to the Southern Region. Scrapped by Medway Secondary Metals, Gillingham at Wimbledon 9/82, except for the wagon on which the cranes were mounted, that being broken up at Ashford Works 12/83.

DRB 78118   DM 721282   TRU 7   –   1965
Allocated to the Southern Region. Scrapped by British Contractors Plant, Staines at Wimbledon 9/82, except for the wagon on which the cranes were mounted, that being broken up at Ashford Works 12/83.

DRB 78119   DS 3148   TRU 12   –   1969
Allocated to the Southern Region. Sent to Horwich Works for stripping in 1982 and broken up at Shildon Works in 1983.

DRB 78120   DS 3147   TRU 13   –   1969
Initially allocated to the Southern Region. Sent to Horwich Works in 1982 and subsequently used in the development of the Plasser Piling machine LDRP 96511. Scrapped at Doncaster Wood Yard by Howard and Wheeler, Ecclesfield 7/90.

DRB 78122   DB 966023   TRM 17   –   1975
Allocated to the London Midland Region. Scrapped at Crewe Gresty Road by Parkes, Oswestry 4/89.

Self-Propelled Heavy Duty Twin Jib Crane

Current Stock:

DRS 78202	DB 965246	78/010	25949 1964	Crewe
DRS 78203	DB 965247	78/012	25950 1965	Leeds
DRS 78204	DB 965406	TRM 6	25636 1963	Crewe
DRS 78206	DB 965408	TRM 8	25895 1964	Merseyside
DRS 78208	DB 965285	TRU 9	26286 1966	Ashford Crane Repair Depot OOU
DRS 78209	DB 965286	TRU 10	26287 1966	Crewe Basford Hall OOU
DRS 78210	DB 965287	TRU 11	26288 1966	Southern Central
DRP 78211	DB 969044	–	6501 1977	Crewe
DRP 78212	DB 969045	–	6502 1978	Bristol
DRP 78213	DB 969046	–	6503 1978	Birmingham
DRP 78214	DB 969047	–	6504 1979	Stratford
DRP 78215	DB 969048	–	6505 1979	South Wales
DRP 78216	DB 969049	–	6506 1979	Southern SW
DRP 78217	DB 969050	–	6507 1979	Reading
DRP 78218	DB 969051	–	6508 1979	Stratford
DRP 78219	DB 969052	–	6509 1979	South Wales
DRP 78220	DB 969053	–	6510 1979	Stratford
DRP 78221	DB 969054	–	6511 1980	Southern SW
DRP 78222	DB 969055	–	6512 1980	Southern SE
DRP 78223	DB 969056	–	6513 1980	Southern Central
DRP 78224	DB 969057	–	6514 1980	Southern SE
DRC 78225	DB 969058	–	31449 1979	Manchester
DRC 78226	DB 969059	–	31450 1980	Scottish SE
DRC 78227	DB 969060	–	31451 1980	Leeds
DRC 78228	DB 969061	–	31452 1980	Birmingham

DRC 78229	DB 969062	–	31453 1980	Glasgow
DRC 78230	DB 969063	–	31454 1980	Nottingham
DRC 78231	DB 969064	–	31455 1980	Leeds
DRC 78232	DB 969065	–	31456 1980	Scottish SE
DRC 78233	DB 969066	–	31457 1980	Preston
DRC 78234	DB 969067	–	31458 1980	Glasgow
DRC 78235	DB 969068	–	31459 1980	Newcastle
DRC 78236	DB 969069	–	31460 1980	Watford
DRC 78237	DB 969070	–	31461 1980	Glasgow
DRC 78238	DB 969071	–	31462 1980	Watford

Vehicles no longer in stock:

DRT 78200	DB 965244	78/008	1781 1965

Allocated to the Eastern Region. Scrapped at Leeds Holbeck by Howard and Wheeler, Ecclesfield 9/87.

DRT 78201	DB 965245	78/009	1782 1965

Allocated to the Eastern Region. Scrapped at Leeds Holbeck by Howard and Wheeler, Ecclesfield 9/87.

DRS 78205	DB 965407	TRM 7	25637 1963

Allocated to the London Midland Region. Broken up at Horwich Works 4/82.

DRS 78207	DB 965284	TRU 8	26285 1966

Allocated to the Southern Region. Scrapped at Hoo Jn. by Morris, Romford 12/89.

SINGLE LINE TRACK RELAYERS (VARIOUS MANUFACTURERS)

A different method of presentation is required for these machines as they do not run on standard gauge track at any time, being carried on wagons. Thus no prefix letters are carried, which means of course that the builder cannot be identified as with other machines in this section.

Secmafer/Tecfer Track Relayer

Current Stock:

	Builder	Type	Wagon	Allocation
78337	Secmafer	Regulator	DB 904630	Western Region
78338	Secmafer	Rail Positioner	DB 976040	Western Region

Vehicles no longer in stock:

The fact that these vehicles do not run on standard gauge track means that the normal methods of disposal are often not used, as of course the wagons on which they are mounted are still retained for further use. Details are therefore only given of builders details, type and final regional allocation of vehicles no longer in stock. Mention should be made that five gantries were sold to the Mid-Hants Railway who in turn resold them to Grant Lyon Eagre. All five were scrapped by 1988.

	Builders Details		Type	Final Regional Allocation
78300	Secmafer	127 1964	M6 Gantry	Scottish
78301	Secmafer	128 1964	M6 Gantry	Scottish
78302	Secmafer	130 1964	M6 Gantry	Southern
78303	Secmafer	131 1964	M6 Gantry	Southern
78304	Secmafer	269 1971	M9 Gantry	Scottish
78305	Secmafer	270 1971	M9 Gantry	Scottish
78306	Arneke		Gantry	Eastern
78307	Arneke		Gantry	Eastern
78308	Arneke		Gantry	Eastern
78309	Secmafer	176 1965	M8 Gantry	London Midland
78310	Secmafer	177 1965	M8 Gantry	London Midland
78311	Secmafer	178 1965	M8 Gantry	Scottish
78312	Secmafer	179 1965	M8 Gantry	Scottish
78313	Secmafer	180 1965	M8 Gantry	London Midland
78314	Secmafer	181 1965	M8 Gantry	London Midland
78315	Secmafer	143 1964	M8 Gantry	Scottish
78316	Secmafer	144 1964	M8 Gantry	Scottish
78317	Secmafer	1662 1964	M6 Gantry	Southern
78318	Secmafer	4662 1964	M6 Gantry	Southern

78319	Secmafer	185 1964	M6 Gantry	Western
78320	Secmafer	186 1964	M6 Gantry	Western
78321	Secmafer	201 1969	M9 Gantry	Scottish
78322	Secmafer	202 1969	M9 Gantry	Scottish
78323	Secmafer	264 1971	M9 Gantry	Western
78324	Secmafer	265 1971	M9 Gantry	Western
78325	Secmafer		M9 Gantry	Western
78326	Secmafer		M9 Gantry	Western
78327	Secmafer	187 1964	M6 Gantry	Southern
78328	Secmafer	188 1964	M6 Gantry	Southern
78329	Secmafer	145 1964	M6 Gantry	Southern
78330	Secmafer	146 1964	M6 Gantry	Southern
78331	Secmafer	147 1964	M6 Gantry	Southern
78332	Secmafer	148 1964	M6 Gantry	Southern
78333	Secmafer		Beam	Scottish
78334	Secmafer		Regulator	Eastern
78335	Secmafer		Rail Positioner	Scottish
78336	Secmafer		Beam	Western
78339	Secmafer		Beam	Western
78340	Secmafer		Regulator	Eastern
78341	Secmafer		Rail Positioner	Western
78343	Tecfer		Gantries with beam	Scottish
78344	Tecfer		Gantries with beam	Eastern
78345	Tecfer		Gantries with beam	Eastern

Donelli PD 350 Single Line Track Relayer

Current Stock:

	Builders Details	Wagon	Allocation
78400	F80216 1980	DE 278482	Stratford
78401	F80217 1980	DM 700715	Stratford
78402	F81242 1981	DB 905097	Leeds
78403	F81243 1981	DB 905089	Leeds
78404	F81232 1981	DM 700724	Crewe
78405	F81233 1981	DB 904696	Crewe
78406	F81250 1981	DB 904519	Stratford
78407	F81251 1981	DB 904524	Stratford
78408	F81248 1981	DE 230964	Perth OOU
78409	F81249 1981	DE 278485	Perth OOU
78410	F81234 1981	DB 904716	Scottish NE
78411	F81235 1981	DB 904520	Scottish NE
78412	F81236 1981	DM 700709	Scottish NE
78413	F81237 1981	DB 904510	Scottish NE
78414	F81229 1981	DS 61154	Leeds
78415	F81228 1981	DE 263284	Leeds
78416	F81226 1981	DE 278494	South Wales
78417	F81227 1981	DE 260861	South Wales
78418	F81244 1981	DB 904631	Newcastle
78419	F81245 1981	DB 904513	Newcastle
78420	F81238 1981	DB 904697	Exeter
78421	F81239 1981	DB 904709	Exeter
78422	F81246 1981	DB 904700	Leeds
78423	F81247 1981	DS 61160	Leeds
78424	F81252 1981	DB 904503	Scottish NE
78425	F81253 1981	DM 700702	Scottish NE
78426	F81240 1981	DB 904525	Leeds
78427	F81241 1981	DS 61151	Leeds

Note: The wagons on which these gantries are mounted frequently interchange.

Bruff Profiler and Grader

Current Stock:

	Builders Details	*Wagon*	*Allocation*
78501	603 1986	DB 994225	Western Region
78502	602 1986	DB 994717	Western Region
78503	601 1986	DB 994209	Eastern Region
78504	605 1986	DB 994090	Eastern Region
78505	604 1986	DB 994341	London Midland Region

Zet Cat Profiler and Grader

Current Stock:

08000   BREL Glasgow 1984   DB 998543   Kilmarnock OOU

Note: Not allocated a number in the 785XX number series.

Donelli PD350 single line track relayers 78418/9 are seen at work near Morpeth on 20th June 1988.
Alan Glen

CRANES

RCE 8XXXX CRANES

As will be seen from the accompanying tables the Director of Civil Engineering has under his control a variety of rail-mounted cranes the types consisting of steam, diesel-mechanical, diesel-electric and diesel-hydraulic. Lifting capacities range from 3 t to 18 t and a wide variety of manufacturers are represented. Lifting capacities up to and including 8 t are classified as light duty, whilst those exceeding 8 t are classified as heavy duty.

Cranes are used for most aspects of the civil engineer's functions such as replacement bridge structures, switch and crossing replacement, track panels and general yard duties. In 1975 a new specification was introduced for a single jib crane to handle switch and crossing renewals, but also capable of being used in a variety of permanent way functions and therefore described as a general purpose crane. Plasser supplied 81503–32 whilst Cowans Sheldon supplied 81533–46. Although each type of crane was built to the same general specifications, each manufacturer was able to develop his own designs within the framework laid down. Lifting capacity is 12 t and when not operational the crane jib stows within its own length for in-train or self-propelled travel.

The delivery of 81503–46 meant the almost complete demise of the surviving steam cranes (80XXX) and also some of the earlier diesel mechanical cranes which were life-expired and becoming increasingly costly to operate because of a lack of spares and subsequent poor availability. Two RCE steam cranes survive, but both are out of use and awaiting disposal. All the 801XX cranes had a lifting capacity of 10 t except for 80115/6/22/3 which were all 15 t.

The light duty diesel mechanical cranes that survive are all being used as yard cranes and can be found at the locations detailed. All eight of the 4 t Jones cranes were purchased secondhand from the Department of the Environment in 1972. All the heavy duty diesel mechanical cranes are 10 t except for DRS 81139 which was 15 t.

The light duty diesel-electric cranes are mainly used as yard cranes (except for DRT 81201/2) and they can be found at the locations detailed. The first heavy duty diesel electric cranes were purchased by the LMR in 1950/1 and had the engine and generator in a separate housing on the carriage of the machine. DRT 81350–9, as they are now numbered are 8½ t cranes.

Only three light duty diesel-hydraulic cranes have been acquired by British Railways all being Jones cranes mounted by BR on wagons. DRJ 81401/3/4 all had a 6 t lifting capacity being mounted on DM 748338, DB 994161 and DB 994969 respectively. Two experimental diesel hydraulic cranes were built by Thomas Smith with a 18 t lifting capacity and had two rotating superstructures geared to rotate in opposite directions, one being a full crane and the other being a slave counterweight. This equalised the weight on the axles when travelling in train formation and gave acceptable stability. DRS 81501/2 have locomotive type cabs and can travel at 35 mph with a staff coach. Thus they are able to travel anywhere without a locomotive being required. This facility is not possible with any other cranes. The new generation of cranes have already been referred to, the balance of the diesel hydraulic fleet being made up of DRA 81547–56. All are now 15 t cranes, 81547–51 having been uprated from 10 t.

Finally, as regards allocations it has been necessary to vary the presentation used according to the region, as the same operational methods are not used throughout British Railways. The Scottish, London Midland and Western Regions are listed by their area allocation, whilst the Eastern and Southern Regions are listed by their depot allocation. As already mentioned, yard cranes of any region are listed at the depot at which they work.

RCE Light Duty Steam Crane

Vehicles no longer in stock:

DRM 80000   –   RS 1034/5   –1939
Allocated to the Glasgow North Division. Sold from Shettleston to the Royal Scottish Museum, Edinburgh 3/82, and now at the Scottish Railway Preservation at Boness.

DRM 80001   –   RS 1035/7   4078 1927
Allocated to the Scottish NE Division. Sold from Perth to the Royal Scottish Museum, Edinburgh 5/83, and now at the Scottish Railway Preservation Society at Boness.

DRG 80002   DB 966281   80/017   2817 1951
Initially allocated to the M & EE Stratford. Later RCE Doncaster. Scrapped at Doncaster by Webster, Dinnington 3/82.

DRS 80003   DB 967307   80/021   17925 1948
Allocated to Low Fell. Disposed of for scrap during 1975.

DRG 80004   DB 967309   80/022   2852 1954
Initially allocated to Drypool. Later Crofton. Scrapped at Ward, Tinsley Works, Sheffield 4/83.

DRT 80005   DB 966216   80/032   1666 1953
Initially allocated to Ipswich Motive Power Depot. Later York Leeman Road. Scrapped at York by Wath Skip Hire, Bolton on Dearne 9/84.

RCE Heavy Duty Steam Crane

Current Stock:

DRC 80115	DB 967303	80/020	8741 1946	York Leeman Road OOU
DRC 80116	DB 967321	80/024	8742 1946	York Leeman Road OOU

Vehicles no longer in stock:

DRG 80100   –   RS 1070/10   2712 1945
Allocated to the Glasgow North Division. Scrapped at Shettleston by Hepburn, Coatbridge 3/82.

DRG 80101   DB 967327   RS 327/10   2886 1954
Initially allocated to Darlington as 80/028. Sent on loan to Glasgow South Division but never returned to Eastern Region. Scrapped at Shettleston by Hepburn, Coatbridge 3/82.

DRG 80102   DB 967328   RS 328/10   2894 1954
Initially allocated to Low Fell. Transferred to Glasgow South Division. Sold from Rutherglen and scrapped at Cohen, Motherwell 1/81.

DRG 80103   DB 966201   80/001   2837 1952
Initially allocated to Beighton. Later Doncaster. Sold from Norwich to the Colne Valley Railway 11/81.

DRT 80104   DE 330205   80/002   1510 1942
Initially allocated to Doncaster. Later Beighton. Scrapped at Beighton by Texas Metal Industries, Hyde 3/82.

DRG 80105   DB 966212   80/003   2825 1952
Allocated to Doncaster. Scrapped at Doncaster by Sheard, Wakefield 3/84.

DRG 80106   DB 966215   80/004   2824 1951
Initially allocated to Peterborough. Later Doncaster. Scrapped at Doncaster by Coopers (Metals) Sheffield 3/84.

DRG 80107   DE 330222   80/005   2529 1940
Initially allocated to Cambridge. Scrapped at Norwich by Texas Metal Industries, Hyde 8/82.

DRG 80108   DE 330225   80/007   2408 1931
Initially allocated to Hunslet. Later York, then Darlington and Doncaster. Scrapped at Dinsdale by Dinsdale Metal Processors, Dinsdale 5/82.

DRG 80109   DE 330250   80/010   2514 1939
Allocated to Low Fell. Scrapped at Low Fell by Seagrave, West Auckland 12/82.

DRA 80110   DE 902250   80/011   5002 1944
Initially brought by BTDB Hull. To York 1968. Disposed of for scrap during 1975.

DRG 80111   DE 330252   80/012   2516 1938
Initially allocated to Beighton. Later Doncaster, and then Crofton. Sold from Crofton to the Keighley and Worth Valley Railway 3/82.

DRG 80112   DB 966271   80/013   2838 1952
Initially allocated to Leyton. Later York. Scrapped at York by Clancey, York 6/82.

DRT 80113   DE 330274   80/015   1576 1945
Initially allocated to Leyton. Later Beighton and then York. Sold from York to the Nene Valley Railway 3/82.

DRG 80114   DB 966280   80/016   2815 1951
Initially allocated to M & EE Stratford. Later Hitchin and then Crofton and Ipswich. Broken up at Doncaster Works 3/78.

DRG 80117   DE 331322   80/025   2536 1939
Initially allocated to Darlington . Later York and then Crofton. Sold from Norwich to the North Norfolk Railway 11/81.

DRG 80118   DB 967325   80/026   2884 1954
Initially allocated to York. Later Leyton and Hitchin. Finally Low Fell. Scrapped at Low Fell by Shepherds Scrap Metals, Newcastle 8/84.

DRG 80119   DB 967326   80/027   2885 1954
Initially allocated to Hunslet. Later Darlington. Then Low Fell and Crofton. Scrapped at Low Fell by Ward, Sheffield 11/81.

DRG 80120   DB 967327   80/028   2886 1954
DUPLICATE CEPS NUMBER ISSUED – SEE DRG 80101.

DRG 80121   DB 967329   80/029   2895 1954
Initially allocated to Low Fell. Later Crofton. Returned to Low Fell. Scrapped at Low Fell by Seagrave, West Auckland 12/82.

DRT 80122   DB 967330   80/030   1698 1955
Initially allocated to Low Fell. Later Crofton. Returned to Low Fell. Scrapped at Low Fell by Texas Metal Industries, Hyde 9/85.

DRT 80123   DB 967331   80/031   1699 1955
Initially allocated to Low Fell. Later Crofton. Returned to Low Fell. Scrapped at Low Fell by Cartwright, Bilston 1/86.

DRT 80130   –   DS 56   1693 1955
Initially allocated to New Cross Gate. Later Hither Green. Scrapped at Ashford PAD by Smeeth Metal, Meopham 6/82.

DRT 80131   –   DS 57   1694 1955
Initially allocated to Beddington Lane. Later Woking. Sold from Eastleigh PAD to the Midland Railway Trust, Butterley 10/82.

DRT 80132   –   DS 58   1695 1955
Initially allocated to Woking. Sold from Eastleigh PAD to the Mid-Hants. Railway 6/83.

DRT 80133   –   DS 414   1595 1948
Allocated to Eastleigh. Sold from Eastleigh PAD to the Mid-Hants. Railway 6/83.

DRT 80134   –   DS 416   1597 1948
Allocated to Ashford. Scrapped at Ashford PAD by Smeeth Metal, Meopham 6/82.

DRT 80135   –   DS 451   1603 1948
Initially allocated to Three Bridges. Sold from Ashford PAD to the Kent and East Sussex Railway 9/82.

DRT 80136   –   DS 452   1604 1948
Initially allocated to Three Bridges. Scrapped at Ashford PAD by Smeeth Metal, Meopham 6/82.

DRT 80137   –   DS 1579   1578 1946
Allocated to Three Bridges. Broken up at Three Bridges by BR 11/80.

DRT 80138   –   DS 1723   1507 1942
Initially allocated to Hither Green. Scrapped at Ashford PAD by Medway Secondary Metals, Gillingham 9/82.

DRT 80139   –   DS 1997   1538 1945
Allocated to Eastleigh. Scrapped at Eastleigh PAD by Brown and Mason, Sandwich 9/82.

DRT 80154   –   DW 154   1596 1948
Initially allocated to the Southern Region as DS 415. To Western Region 1963. Allocated to Taunton. Stripped for spares to maintain sister cranes and broken up at Swindon Works 9/77.

DRT 80168   –   DW 68   1598 1948
Initially allocated to Swindon. Later Gloucester and then Plymouth. Broken up at Swindon Works 11/77.

DRT 80169   –   DW 69   1599 1948
Allocated to the Reading Division. Later Exeter Division. Scrapped at Plymouth, Tavistock Jn. by Plant Dismantlers, Plymouth 7/81.

DRT 80172   –   DW 72   1600 1948
Allocated to the Bristol Division. Broken up at Taunton by BR 10/82.

DRT 80173   –   DW 73   1601 1948
Allocated to the Swansea Division. Sold from Danygraig and scrapped at Steel Supply, Swansea 6/81.

RCE Light Duty Diesel Mechanical Cranes

Current Stock:

DRT 81025	–	DM 1425	1675 1955	Northampton CMD OOU
DRT 81026	–	DM 1426	1676 1955	Crewe Gresty Lane
DRT 81027	–	DM 1427	1677 1955	Northampton CMD
DRT 81028	–	DM 1428	1678 1955	Crewe Basford Hall OOU

Vehicles no longer in stock:

DRJ 81000   DB 965920   RD 1168/4   10073 1953
Acquired secondhand from the Department of the Environment in 1972. Allocated to the Glasgow South Division for use at Rutherglen. Scrapped at Rutherglen by a private contractor 11/83.

DRJ 81001   DB 965921   RD 1169/4   10072 1953
Acquired secondhand from the Department of the Environment in 1972. Allocated to the Scottish South East Division for use at Millerhill. Scrapped at Millerhill by a private contractor 11/83.

DRG 81002   DB 967481   81/008   2955 1956
Allocated to York Concrete Works. Scrapped at York Concrete Works by Texas Metal Industries, Hyde 2/85.

DRT 81003   –   DM 1403   1391 1939
Initially allocated to the Preston Division. Later Liverpool Division. Scrapped at Fazakerley by Oldham Bros, Liverpool 12/82.

DRT 81004   –   DM 1401   1388 1939
Allocated to the Nottingham Division. Scrapped at Lenton by Cooper, Swindon 7/82.

DRT 81006   –   DM 1406   1415 1940
Allocated to the Crewe Division. Broken up at Horwich Works 2/82.

DRT 81007   –   DM 1407   1416 1940
Allocated to the Nottingham Division. Scrapped at Lenton by Corbard Contractors, Nottingham 3/81.

DRT 81008   –   DM 1408   1417 1940
Allocated to the Liverpool Division. Scrapped at Crewe ETD by Ward, Sheffield 12/81.

DRT 81009   –   DM 1409   1418 1940
Allocated to the Liverpool Division. Later Manchester Division. Scrapped at Castleton by Ward, Sheffield 2/82.

DRJ 81022   DB 966440   81/022   10057 1953
Acquired secondhand from the Department of the Environment in 1972. Allocated to Dinsdale. Scrapped at Dinsdale by Herring, Hartlepool 8/87.

DRJ 81023   DB 966441   81/023   10061 1953
Acquired second hand from the Department of the Environment in 1972. Allocated to Crofton. Scrapped at Crofton by Sheard, Wakefield 5/88.

DRT 81030   –   DM 1430   1713 1957
Allocated to the Preston Division. Broken up at Derby Works 12/82.

DRT 81031   –   DM 1431   1714 1957
Also numbered 55095 whilst in internal use at Doncaster Works but now transferred to D of M & EE – See ADRT 96031.

DRT 81032   –   DM 1432   1715 1957
Allocated to the Manchester Division. Broken up at Derby Loco Works 11/81.

DRT 81033   –   DM 1433   1716 1958
Allocated to the Watford Division. Broken up at Horwich Works 2/82.

DRS 81040   –   DM 1440   20877 1954
Initially allocated to the Western Region as DB 346. Later transferred to Birmingham Division. Scrapped at Wolverhampton (Wednesfield Road) by Casbern Metals, Stoke 5/82.

DRJ 81050   –   DS 1800   10065 1953
Acquired secondhand from the Department of th Environment in 1972. Allocated to Redbridge. Scrapped at Redbridge by Rollason, Telford 12/86.

DRJ 81051   –   DS 1690   10048 1953
Acquired secondhand from the Department of the Environment in 1972. Allocated to Redbridge. Dismantled to provide spares for DRJ 81052. Remains scrapped at Redbridge by Rollason, Telford 12/86.

DRJ 81052   –   DS 1691   10064 1953

Acquired secondhand from the Department of the Environment in 1972. Allocated to Redbridge. Rebuilt using parts from DRJ 81051. Scrapped at Redbridge by Rollason, Telford 12/86.

DRJ 81053   –   DS 1692   10066 1953

Acquired secondhand from the Department of the Environment in 1972. Allocated to New Cross Gate. Scrapped at New Cross Gate by a private contractor in 1986.

RCE Heavy Duty Diesel Mechanical Cranes

Current Stock:

DRT 81100	–	RD 1150/10	1625 1950	Crofton
DRT 81101	–	RD 1151/10	1626 1950	Crofton OOU
DRT 81123	–	DM 1423	1668 1953	Doncaster OOU
DRT 81129	–	DM 1429	1624 1949	Doncaster
DRT 81134	–	DM 1434	1701 1957	Doncaster OOU
DRT 81137	–	DM 1437	1704 1957	Crofton
DRT 81138	–	DM 1438	1705 1957	Crofton
DRT 81142	DB 966403	81/003	1623 1950	Doncaster OOU
DRT 81143	DB 967478	81/006	1671 1954	Crofton OOU
DRT 81144	DB 967479	81/007	1672 1954	Norwich

Vehicles no longer in stock:

DRT 81105   –   DM 1402   1390 1939

Allocated to the Liverpool Division. Later Preston Division. Scrapped at Warrington Arpley by Chadwick, Stalybridge 11/81.

DRT 81110   –   DM 1410   1490 1940

Allocated to the Crewe Division. Transferred to internal use at Derby Locomotive Works 11/81.

DRT 81111   –   DM 1411   1511 1942

Allocated to the Crewe Division. Broken up at Derby Works 7/82.

DRT 81112   –   DM 1412   1512 1942

Allocated to the Watford Division. Damaged in an accident at Bedford 12/77 and sent to Horwich Works. Subsequently moved to Doncaster Works where it was broken up 11/80.

DRT 81113   –   DM 1413   1513 1942

Allocated to the Nottingham Division. Scrapped at Lenton by Cooper, Swindon 7/82.

DRT 81114   –   DM 1414   1514 1942

Allocated to the Watford Division. Scrapped at Northampton by Cartwright, Tipton 3/83.

DRS 81118   –   DM 1418   18976 1951

Allocated to the Nottingham Division. Scrapped at Lenton by Cooper, Swindon 7/82.

DRS 81119   –   DM 1419   18977 1951

Allocated to the Manchester Division. Scrapped at Castleton by Ward, Sheffield 5/82.

DRS 81120   –   DM 1420   18978 1952

Allocated to the Birmingham Division. Scrapped at Lenton by Cooper, Swindon 7/82.

DRS 81121   –   DM 1421   18979 1952

Allocated to the Liverpool Division. Scrapped at Rugby by Ward, Sheffield 7/82.

DRT 81124   –   DM 1424   1667 1953

Initially allocated to the Watford Division. Transferred to the Eastern Region 1980. Allocated to Cambridge. Scrapped at Leeds Holbeck by Sheard, Wakefield 9/87.

DRT 81135   –   DM 1435   1702 1957

Initially allocated to the Liverpool Division. Transferred to the Eastern Region 1980. Allocated to Doncaster. Stripped for spares to maintain sister cranes and broken up at York WRD 6/86.

DRT 81136   –   DM 1436   1703 1957

Allocated to the Liverpool Division. Transferred to the Eastern Region 1980. Allocated to York. Scrapped at York WRD by Clancey, York 7/89.

DRT 81139   –   DM 1439   23613 1957

Allocated to the Manchester Division for use at Newton Heath RCE Depot. Sold from Newton Heath to Texas Metal Industries, Hyde 6/90. Resold to Norton, Trafford Park. Then resold again to Peak Rail 9/90.

DRS 81140   DB 966401   81/001   24247 1957

Initially allocated to Hitchin. To York Concrete Yard 1983. Sold from York to Booth, Rotherham 6/87. Resold to the Stephenson Museum, Chirton.

DRS 81141   DB 966402   81/002   24245 1957
Initially allocated to Hitchin. Later Crofton. Scrapped at Leeds Holbeck by Robinson and Birdsall, Leeds 11/83.

RCE Light Duty Diesel Electric Cranes

Current Stock:

DRT 81201	–	RDE 1159/7	1738 1960	Preston
DRT 81202	–	RDE 1160/7	1739 1960	Kilmarnock OOU
DRS 81257	–	DB 357	24593 1961	Radyr

Vehicles no longer in stock:

DRF 81200   –   RDE 1153/7   15416 1953
Allocated to the Glasgow South Division for use at Rutherglen. Scrapped at Rutherglen by Lowmac Alloys, Ayr 4/86.

DRF 81203   DB 965922   RDE 1170/4   14101 1953
Acquired second hand from the Department of the Environment in 1972 Allocated to Dalmeny for use on the Forth Bridge. Scrapped at Dalmeny by A–Z Mechanical Engineers, Doncaster 7/90.

DRS 81258   –   DB 358   24595 1961
Allocated to Radyr. Broken up at Swindon Works during 1986.

DRS 81259   –   DB 359   24594 1961
Initially allocated to Hookagate. Later Radyr. Scrapped at Radyr by Rogers, Cardiff 5/89.

DRT 81264   –   RDE 1764   1741 1960
Allocated to the Manchester Division. Scrapped at Rugby by Berry, Leicester 6/88.

RCE Heavy Duty Diesel Electric Cranes

Current Stock:

DRT 81300	–	RDE 1162/10	1742 1960	Polmadie OOU
DRT 81301	–	RDE 1163/10	1743 1960	Kilmarnock OOU
DRT 81302	–	RDE 1164/10	1751 1961	Scottish NE
DRT 81303	–	RDE 1165/10	1752 1961	Rutherglen OOU
DRT 81304	DB 965334	RDE 1166/12	1799 1969	Rutherglen OOU
DRT 81305	DB 965335	RDE 1167/12	1801 1969	Polmadie OOU
DRF 81306	DB 966417	81/021	16963 1958	Crofton
DRT 81307	DB 967476	81/004	1682 1955	Crofton OOU
DRT 81308	DB 967477	81/005	1683 1955	Crofton OOU
DRF 81309	DB 967482	81/009	16208 1958	Crofton
DRF 81310	DB 967483	81/010	16209 1958	Crofton
DRF 81311	DB 967484	81/011	17454 1958	Crofton
DRF 81312	DB 967490	81/012	17820 1959	Crofton
DRF 81313	DB 967491	81/013	17821 1959	Low Fell
DRF 81314	DB 967492	81/014	17822 1959	Low Fell
DRF 81315	DB 967493	81/015	17823 1959	Low Fell
DRT 81316	DB 966437	81/016	1798 1969	Ashford Crane Repair Depot OOU
DRT 81317	DB 966438	81/017	1800 1969	Radyr OOU
DRT 81318	DB 966439	81/018	1802 1969	Kilmarnock OOU
DRC 81319	DB 965945	81/025	30304 1972	Beighton
DRC 81320	DB 965948	81/026	30307 1972	Beighton
DRF 81321	DB 967486	81/024	17372 1958	Beighton
DRC 31322	DB 965944	RDE 1171/12	30303 1972	Crofton
DRF 81323	DB 967487	–	17373 1958	Chesterton Jn.
DRS 81330	DB 965153	–	24610 1959	Woking
DRS 81331	DB 965154	–	24611 1959	Three Bridges
DRS 81332	DB 965155	–	24612 1959	Leyton OOU
DRS 81333	DB 965156	–	24613 1959	Leyton OOU
DRS 81334	DB 965171	–	25333 1962	Ashford
DRS 81336	DB 965173	–	25335 1962	Eastleigh PAD OOU
DRC 81337	DB 965943	–	30302 1972	Beighton
DRT 81338	DB 965288	–	1791 1969	Three Bridges
DRT 81339	DB 965289	–	1792 1969	Woking
DRT 81340	DB 965290	–	1794 1969	Hither Green
DRT 81341	DB 965291	–	1795 1969	Ashford
DRT 81342	DB 965292	–	1796 1969	Three Bridges
DRT 81343	DB 965293	–	1797 1969	Eastleigh

DRT 81350	–	DM 1750	1633	1950	Watford
DRT 81351	–	DM 1751	1634	1950	Crewe Gresty Road OOU
DRT 81352	–	DM 1752	1635	1950	Watford
DRT 81353	–	DM 1753	1636	1951	Crewe
DRT 81354	–	DM 1754	1637	1951	Watford
DRT 81355	–	DM 1755	1638	1951	Crewe Gresty Road OOU
DRT 81356	–	DM 1756	1639	1951	Crewe
DRT 81357	–	DM 1757	1640	1951	Watford
DRT 81358	–	DM 1758	1641	1951	Crewe
DRT 81359	–	DM 1759	1642	1951	Nottingham
DRT 81362	DB 965332	–	1793	1969	Reading
DRC 81363	DB 965946	–	30305	1972	Crofton
DRT 81367	–	DM 1767	1744	1960	Crewe

Vehicles no longer in stock:

DRS 81335   DB 965172   –   25334 1962
Initially allocated to Hither Green. Later Redbridge. Sold from Eastleigh PAD to the Dart Valley Railway 8/89.

DRT 81368   –   DM 1768   1745 1960
Initially allocated to the Watford Division. Later Nottingham Division. Stripped for spares to maintain sister cranes and broken up at Lenton by BR during 1987.

DRT 81369   –   DM 1769   1746 1960
Allocated to the Nottingham Division. Initially sold from Crewe Gresty Road to the Dart Valley Railway 8/89. Damaged at Bescot and scrapped there by Hampton, Keele 6/90.

DRC 81373   DB 965947   DM 1773   30306 1972
Transferred to D of M & EE in 1988 – See ADRC 96418

RCE Light Duty Diesel Hydraulic Cranes

Current Stock:

DRJ 81401   –   DM 1701   –   1969   Willesden Old Oak Sidings OOU

Vehicles no longer in stock:

DRJ 81403   –   DM 1703   –   1975
Allocated to the Crewe Division. Scrapped at Stoke by Poole, Hanley 7/84.

DRJ 81404   –   DM 1704   –   1975
Initially allocated to the Preston Division. Later Liverpool Division. Scrapped at Carnforth by Taylor, Bury 6/84.

RCE Heavy Duty Diesel Hydraulic Cranes

Current Stock:

DRS 81501	DB 965348	81/020	26678	1971	York Leeman Road OOU
DRS 81502	–	DM 1702	26679	1971	To be transferred from LMR–WR
DRP 81503	DB 969000	–	5501	1977	Watford
DRP 81504	DB 969001	–	5502	1978	Watford
DRP 81505	DB 969002	–	5503	1978	Leyton
DRP 81506	DB 969003	–	5504	1978	Hitchin
DRP 81507	DB 969004	–	5505	1978	Hither Green
DRP 81508	DB 969005	–	5506	1979	Three Bridges
DRP 81509	DB 969006	–	5507	1979	Reading
DRP 81510	DB 969007	–	5508	1979/80	Low Fell
DRP 81511	DB 969008	–	5509	1979/80	Woking
DRP 81512	DB 969009	–	5510	1979/80	Doncaster
DRP 81513	DB 969010	–	5511	1980	Eastleigh
DRP 81514	DB 969011	–	5512	1980	Exeter
DRP 81515	DB 969012	–	5513	1980	Low Fell
DRP 81516	DB 969013	–	5514	1980	South Wales
DRP 81517	DB 969014	–	5515	1980	Three Bridges
DRP 81518	DB 969015	–	5516	1980	Crewe
DRP 81519	DB 969016	–	5517	1980	Hither Green
DRP 81520	DB 969017	–	5518	1980	South Wales
DRP 81521	DB 969018	–	5519	1980	Doncaster
DRP 81522	DB 969019	–	5520	1980	Leyton

DRP 81523	DB 969020	–	5521	1980	Bristol
DRP 81524	DB 969021	–	5522	1980	Watford
DRP 81525	DB 969022	–	5523	1981	Leyton
DRP 81526	DB 969023	–	5524	1981	Birmingham
DRP 81527	DB 969024	–	5525	1981	York Leeman Road
DRP 81528	DB 969025	–	5526	1981	Hitchin
DRP 81529	DB 969026	–	5527	1981	Nottingham
DRP 81530	DB 969027	–	5528	1981	Crewe
DRP 81531	DB 969028	–	5529	1981	Nottingham
DRP 81532	DB 969029	–	5530	1981	Ashford
DRC 81533	DB 969030	–	31435	1978	Low Fell
DRC 81534	DB 969031	–	31436	1978	Glasgow
DRC 81535	DB 969032	–	31437	1978	Crewe
DRC 81536	DB 969033	–	31438	1978	Glasgow
DRC 81537	DB 969034	–	31439	1978	Norwich
DRC 81538	DB 969035	–	31440	1978	Scottish SE
DRC 81539	DB 969036	–	31441	1979	Preston
DRC 81540	DB 969037	–	31442	1979	Glasgow
DRC 81541	DB 969038	–	31443	1979	Norwich
DRC 81542	DB 969039	–	31444	1979	Manchester
DRC 81543	DB 969040	–	31445	1979	Glasgow
DRC 81544	DB 969041	–	31446	1979	Manchester
DRC 81545	DB 969042	–	31447	1979	Preston
DRC 81546	DB 969043	–	31448	1979	Scottish NE
DRA 81547	–	DB 347	6041	1958	South Wales
DRA 81548	–	DB 348	6042	1958	Reading
DRA 81549	–	DB 349	6043	1958	Exeter
DRA 81551	–	DB 351	6288	1959	South Wales
DRA 81552	–	DB 352	6045	1958	Bristol
DRA 81553	–	DB 353	6046	1958	Reading OOU
DRA 81554	–	DB 354	6047	1958	South Wales
DRA 81555	–	DB 355	6048	1958	South Wales
DRA 81556	–	DB 356	6209	1959	South Wales

Vehicle no longer in stock:

DRA 81550	–	DB 350	6044	1958

Allocated to the Swansea Division. Later Reading Division. Scrapped at Cardiff Cathays by Rogers, Cardiff 4/90.

Plasser GPC-72 diesel hydraulic crane DRP 81504 is seen at Northampton CMD on 25th January 1989.
Colin Underhill

M & EE 9XXXX CRANES

Initially the number series allocated to M & EE cranes were 90XXX and 91XXX, but before any renumberings took place this was changed to 95XXX for steam cranes and 96XXX for diesel cranes. Almost all the cranes within this series are owned by the M & EE the exceptions being identifiable by the prefix carried.

Only one steam crane survives, ADRS 95000 the delightful 3 t crane at Toton still finding occasional use.

The two light duty diesel mechanical cranes were 4 t ADRJ 96000 and 5 t ADRT 96031. Of the heavy duty diesel mechanical cranes ADRC 96100/1 are 30 t whilst ADRS 96102 was a 15 t crane. Both the diesel-mechanical breakdown cranes are 75 t and are allocated to the Southern Region.

The light duty diesel-electric crane fleet consists of 4 t cranes ADRT 96300–6, whilst ADRT 96307–12 are 6½ t. This number series was extended in 1984 by the modification of seven Bogie Bolster wagons to enable them to be fitted with swing jib crane units and other equipment for the transportation and off-loading of electrification structures. An additional ten have been modified in 1985, the crane units being built by Mecan at Rotherham.

The majority of these cranes are used on electrification construction work and at the time of writing are allocated to the depots listed. It should however be emphasised that allocations are variable depending on the workload of the different ECDs at any particular time. Those cranes amongst ADRT 96300–12 which are used almost exclusively by the electrification department are to be officially so transferred and will thus become LDRT instead of ADRT. The heavy duty diesel-electric crane fleet consists of 10 t cranes 96402/4/5/7/8/11/2, 8½ t cranes 96413/4 and 15 t crane 96418. Four numbers in this series were allocated to cranes currently owned by the RCE, 96409/15–7 now being 81323/67–9 respectively.

The builders numbers quoted for the Coles cranes amongst this batch relate to the present day, but mention needs to be made that structure swopping has taken place from time to time and most of these cranes are therefore hybrid. The 965XX series was originally designated as being for 'Light Duty Diesel Hydraulic Cranes,' but as the notes below clearly indicate the series now encompasses a whole variety of miscellaneous lifting and on-track equipment.

ADRW 96500/1 are telescopic 5 t Altas cranes fitted on Warwell wagons and are owned by the Power Supply Section. A similar vehicle KDS 3149 was originally numbered KDRW 96502, but at the request of the S&T has reverted to its original number. Similarly KDRH 96503 is now to be identified by the number of its base vehicle KDB 924203. None of these first four vehicles are self propelled.

LDRP 96504–9 are EPV 360 Rail-mounted excavators whilst LDRP 96510 is a powered base unit which can have variable equipment on top and is known as a PV5. LDRP 96511 is the much publicised SCPV 14 Piling machine developed by BR in conjunction with Plasser, following development trials with redundant track-relayer DRB 78120. LDRP 96511 can move either in train formation or under its own power and mounted on its centre is a crane with a telescopic jib, to which a vibrator can be attached. The frame between the crane and the ends of the vehicle is in the form of a well for storage of piles and the vibrator used to drive the piles into the ground. Initially LDRP 96511 was to be built at Plasser's West Ealing factory and was allocated works number 52947. However it was subsequently decided to build it in Austria. LDRP 96512–4 are GPC-38 cranes whilst also included here for completeness are the six Poclain self-powered excavators initially purchased for the WCML electrification and which are basically an earlier version of LDRP 96504–9. Consideration was given to renumbering them into the 965XX number series, but in view of their short-life expectancy this is now unlikely to occur.

The 966XX number series is reserved for any heavy duty diesel hydraulic cranes that might be acquired, whilst ADRC 96700–15 are the diesel-hydraulic breakdown crane fleet. ADRC 96700–9 were converted from steam at Derby Locomotive Works between 1976–8, whilst ADRC 96710–5 were built as diesel-hydraulic cranes. Various problems with ADRC 96710–5 were experienced and consequently the dates of acceptance into service were rather later than the building dates listed. This also resulted in several switches of identity and those listed reflect the current situation. ADRC 96700–15 are all 76 t breakdown cranes, whilst a conversion programme of five 45 t steam breakdown cranes at Derby Locomotive Works took place in 1985/6, the numbers ADRC 96716–20 being allocated. The allocations listed reflect the current situation but will obviously be variable as cranes currently at Ashford Crane Repair Depot are returned to service.

The 968XX number series was originally allocated to bring electric chain hoist fitted vehicle KDM 720905 into the plant vehicle number series. As with 96502/3, the original number is now being used. Also included here for completeness is KDB 905096 the other S&T vehicle fitted with a hydraulic hoist.

Before concluding this section mention must be made of the late John Brownlie's book 'Railway Steam Cranes'. It really is a most excellent book for anyone wishing to read in great detail about the manufacture and operation of steam cranes from 1875 to the present day.

RM & EE Light Duty Steam Crane

Current Stock:

ADRS 95000   –   ADM 1108   23027 1955   Toton

M & EE Heavy Duty Steam Crane

Vehicle no longer in stock:

ADRG 95100   ADS 1826   2610 1943
10 t crane initially allocated to Eastleigh C & W Works. Later Ashford Works. Since early 1970s allocated to Horsham for the use of the Power Supply Section. Scrapped at Horsham (as ADS 1826) by Phillips (Metals), Llanelli 12/86.

M & EE Breakdown Steam Crane

Vehicles no longer in stock:

ADRC 95200   –   RS 1062/36   3310 1914
Initially allocated to St. Margarets. To Thornton 3/62. To Dundee West 1967. Sold from Carstairs to the Scottish Railway Preservation Society 6/79. Stored at Perth 1988.

ADRR 95201   –   ADS 81   C6553 1927
36 t crane initially allocated to Brighton. To Fratton 1946. To Stewarts Lane 1963. Sold from Stewarts Lane to the Kent and East Sussex Railway 1/87.

ADRC 95202   –   RS 1001/50   5112 1930 rebuilt 6637 1938
Initially allocated to Durran Hill. To Kingmoor 1936. To Lostock Hall 1962. Later Wigan. Sold from Wigan to Midland Railway Trust, Butterley 8/80.

ADRC 95203   –   RS 1005/50   5111 1930 rebuilt 6636 1938
Initially allocated to Leeds. To Crewe 1939. Later Wigan. Sold from Wigan to the Keighley and Worth Valley Railway 5/82.

ADRC 95204   –   RS 1054/50   5113 1930 rebuilt 6638 1938
Initially allocated to Motherwell. To St. Margarets 1961. To Haymarket 1966. Sold from Haymarket to the Great Western Society, Didcot 9/87.

ADRV 95205   –   RS 1013/50   C12683 1931
Initially allocated to Rugby. To Crewe RM & EE 1945. To Bescot 1965. Later Longsight. Finally Carlisle. Sold from Carlisle to the East Lancashire Railway 11/82.

ADRV 95206   –   RS 1015/50   C12683 1931
Initially allocated to Newton Heath. To Willesden 1939. To Derby 1962. To Willesden 1965. Later Allerton. Sold from Allerton to the Dinting Railway Centre 2/82. Transferred to the Keighley and Worth Valley Railway 9/90.

ADRR 95207   –   ADE 331159   D2958 1931
40 t crane initially allocated to Kentish Town. To Leeds 1939. Number changed from RS 1004 when transferred to the NE Region 1954. Sold from Doncaster to Wath Skip Hire, Bolton on Dearne 12/82. Resold to the Nene Valley Railway 1/83.

ADRR 95208   –   RS 1097/45   E8137/8 1940
Initially allocated to GWR at Wolverhampton Stafford Road. To LM Region 1963. Later Oxley, Tyseley and then Saltley. Finally Crewe. Sold from Crewe to the Great Central Railway, Loughborough 2/82.

ADRR 95209   –   ADS 1560   E8133 1940
45 t crane initially allocated to Guildford. Later Nine Elms and Hither Green. Finally Stewarts Lane. Sold from Stewarts Lane to Swindon Railway Engineering Ltd. 6/89 and moved to Swindon 12/90.

ADRR 95210   –   ADS 1561   E8133 1940
45 t crane initially allocated to Guildford, but loaned to Dover for government use 1940–5. To Ashford, Eastleigh and Chart Leacon. Later Brighton and finally Stewarts Lane. Sold from Stewarts Lane to Swindon Railway Engineering Ltd. 6/89 and moved to Swindon 12/90.

ADRR 95211   –   ADW 16   E8137/8 1940
45 t crane allocated to Old Oak Common. Broken up at Swindon Works during 1986.

ADRR 95212   –   ADW 18   E8137/8 1940
45 t crane initially allocated to Cardiff Canton. To Laira 1963 and then Landore 1965. Sold from Old Oak Common to Flying Scotsman Enterprises, Carnforth 2/84.

ADRR 95213   –   ADW 19   E8137/8 1940
45 t crane mainly kept at Swindon Workshops, but made available for breakdown work. Later allocated to Bristol and finally Laira. Sold from Laira to Swindon Works Ltd 12/87.

ADRR 95214   –   ADE 330102   F4991–3 1943
45 t crane initially allocated to Kings Cross. to Grimesthorpe 1961. To Tinsley 1965. Sold from Tinsley to the North Yorkshire Moors Railway 7/86.

ADRR 95215   –   RS 1083/45   F4991–3 1943
Initially allocated to Gorton. Number changed from DE 330122 when transferred to the LM Region in 1960. To Newton Heath 1965. Sold from Newton Heath to the Bluebell Railway 11/81.

ADRR 95216   –   ADW 151   F9162 1945
45 t crane initially allocated to Exmouth Jn. Number changed from DS 1580 when transferred to the Western Region 1963. To Newton Abbot and then Laira. Sold from Old Oak Common to the Gloucestershire–Warwickshire Railway 11/83.

ADRC 95217   –   ADE 331156   6872 1939
Converted to diesel power at Derby Locomotive Works 10/85. See ADRC 96716.

ADRC 95218   –   ADE 330110   6871 1939
Converted to diesel power at Derby Locomotive Works 8/86. See ADRC 96719.

ADRC 95219   –   ADE 330133   6873 1939
Converted to diesel power at Derby Locomotive Works 1/87. See ADRC 96720.

ADRC 95220   –   RS 1058/45   6870 1939
Converted to diesel power at Derby Locomotive Works 10/85. See ADRC 96717.

ADRC 95221   –   RS 1085/45   8053 1943
Converted to diesel power at Derby Locomotive Works 5/86. See ADRC 96718.

ADRC 95222   ADB 966103   –   9017 1948
36 t crane initially allocated to Grimsby. Later Immingham. Finally Thornaby. Sold from Derby Locomotive Works to the Dean Forest Railway 4/86.

ADRC 95223   –   RS 1106/36   5755 1936
Initially allocated to Colwick. Later Toton. Sold from Toton to Peak Rail, Buxton 12/87.

ADRC 95224   –   ADE 330107   4524 1926
45 t crane initially allocated to Doncaster. To Healey Mills 1965. Sold from Healey Mills to the North Yorkshire Moors Railway 4/81.

ADRR 95225   –   ADS 80   C6553 1927
36 t crane initially allocated to Ashford. Later Guildford and Eastleigh. To Hither Green 1967. Finally Stewarts Lane. Scrapped at Stewarts Lane by Stanley, Bexleyheath 3/86.

M & EE Light Duty Diesel Mechanical Crane

Vehicles no longer in stock:

ADRJ 96000   –   ADM 1161   46074 1960
Initially allocated to Dundee. Later Perth when it carried in error the number DRT 81263. Scrapped at Perth by Texas Metal Industries, Hyde 5/89.

ADRT 96031   –   DM 1431   1714 1957
Initially allocated to the Preston Division. Renumbered from DRT 81031 to 55095 whilst in internal use at Doncaster Works. Renumbered to ADRT 96031 when transferred to the D of M&EE at Doncaster Carr. Scrapped at Doncaster Carr by Lincoln Ferrous Metals, Lincoln 10/88.

M & EE Heavy Duty Diesel Mechanical Crane

Current Stock:

ADRC 96100   ADB 965183   –   66 1961   Horsham
ADRC 96101   ADB 965184   –   67 1961   Horsham

Vehicle no longer in stock:

Many of the diesel cranes acquired in the 1950s and 1960s were built by Taylor and Hubbard. This photograph shows ADRT 96302 at Millerhill ECD on 26th August 1990. Roy Hennefer

Plasser EPV 360 Rail-mounted excavator LDRP 96508 is seen at Millerhill ECD on 26th August 1990. Roy Hennefer

ADRS 96102   –   ADM 1417   18528 1950

Initially allocated to the Preston Division. Transferred to the Southern Region in 1980 for use of the Power Supply Section. Scrapped at Ashford Crane Repair Depot by Phillips (Metals), Llanelli 12/86.

M & EE Diesel Mechanical Breakdown Crane

Current Stock:

ADRC 96200	ADB 965185	–	88 1963	Chart Leacon
ADRC 96201	ADB 965186	–	89 1963	Stewarts Lane

M & EE Light Duty Diesel Electric Crane

Current Stock:

ADRT 96301	–	ADM 1761	1718 1958	Crewe Gresty Road OOU
ADRT 96302	–	ADM 1770	1747 1960	Millerhill ECD
ADRT 96303	–	ADM 1771	1748 1961	Heaton ECD
ADRT 96304	–	ADM 1772	1749 1961	Crewe TMD (E)
ADRT 96305	–	RDE 1154/4	1728 1958	Peterborough ECD
ADRT 96306	–	RDE 1155/4	1729 1958	Heaton ECD
ADRT 96307	ADB 966431	–	1724 1958	Heaton ECD
ADRT 96308	ADB 966432	–	1725 1958	Doncaster Hexthorpe ECD OOU
ADRT 96309	ADB 966433	–	1726 1958	Peterborough ECD
ADRT 96310	ADB 966434	–	1727 1958	Romford OHLM
ADRT 96311	–	RDE 1156/6½	1730 1959	Millerhill ECD
ADRT 96312	–	RDE 1157/6½	1731 1959	Peterborough ECD
LDRB 96313	–	LDB 928032	1984	Peterborough ECD
LDRB 96314	–	LDB 928131	1984	Peterborough ECD
LDRB 96315	–	LDB 927956	1984	Peterborough ECD
LDRB 96316	–	LDB 927823	1984	Millerhill ECD
LDRB 96317	–	LDB 928039	1984	Peterborough ECD
LDRB 96318	–	LDB 927917	1984	Peterborough ECD
LDRB 96319	–	LDB 928138	1984	Peterborough ECD
LDRB 96320	–	LDB 927883	1985	Millerhill ECD
LDRB 96321	–	LDB 928051	1985	Millerhill ECD
LDRB 96322	–	LDB 927868	1985	Millerhill ECD
LDRB 96323	–	LDB 928053	1985	Peterborough ECD
LDRB 96324	–	LDB 927813	1985	Doncaster Hexthorpe ECD
LDRB 96325	–	LDB 928016	1985	Peterborough ECD
LDRB 96326	–	LDB 928183	1985	Peterborough ECD
LDRB 96327	–	LDB 928116	1985	Millerhill ECD
LDRB 96328	–	LDB 927865	1985	Peterborough ECD
LDRB 96329	–	LDB 927817	1985	Peterborough ECD

Note: During 1991 and the first half of 1992 a significant number of the vehicles detailed above will be based at Kings Norton ECD for use on the electrification of Birmingham's Cross-City line.

Vehicle no longer in stock:

ADRT 96300   –   ADM 1760   1717 1958

Initially used on the WCML electrification. Later Liverpool and Manchester Divisions. Stored at Crewe TMD (E). Scrapped at Booth Roe Metals Rotherham 6/88.

M & EE and Operating Department Heavy Duty Diesel Electric Crane

Current Stock:

ADRF 96402	ADB 966407	–	16986 1958	Doncaster Carr
TDRF 96404	TDB 966409	–	15960 1958	Tinsley Yard OOU
ADRF 96405	ADB 966410	–	15962 1958	Gateshead
ADRF 96407	ADB 966412	–	17370 1958	Lincoln
ADRF 96408	ADB 966414	–	17371 1958	Tinsley Yard OOU
TDRF 96411	TDB 967489	–	17600 1958	Tinsley Yard OOU
ADRT 96412	ADB 966435	–	1740 1960	Romford OHLM
ADRT 96413	–	DM 1762	1734 1959	Stafford
ADRT 96414	–	DM 1763	1735 1959	Heaton ECD
ADEC 96418	DB 965947	DM 1773	30306 1972	Romford OHLM

ADEC 96418   DB 965947   DM 1773   30306 1972   Romford OHLM

Note: 96409/15–7 are now numbered 81323/67–9 respectively

Vehicles no longer in stock:

ADRF 96400   ADB 966405   –   15958 1958
Initially allocated to Hull Dairycoates. Later Doncaster Carr, where it was scrapped by Lincoln Ferrous Metals, Lincoln 10/88.

TDRF 96401   TDB 966406   –   16981 1958
Allocated to the Leeds Division. Scrapped at Leeds Holbeck by Booth, Rotherham 10/87.

TDRF 96403   TDB 966408   –   15964 1958
Initially allocated to Temple Mills. Later Beighton. Scrapped at Tinsley Yard by Berry, Leicester 6/88.

TDRF 96406   TDB 966411   –   15965 1958
Allocated to the Sheffield Division. Broken up at Doncaster Carr by BR 5/84.

TDRF 96410   TDB 967488   –   17599 1958
Initially allocated to York. Later Leeds Holbeck and then Colchester. Finally Romford, where it was scrapped by Morris, Romford 4/88.

Miscellaneous Lifting and On-Track Equipment

(Number series officially designated 'Miscellaneous Light Duty Diesel Hydraulic Cranes')

Current Stock:

ADRW 96500	–	ADS 3146	1973	Horsham
ADRW 96501	–	ADS 3150	1973	Horsham
(KDRW 96502)	–	KDS 3149	1981	York Leeman Road
(KDRH 96503)	–	KDB 924203	6877 1978	Tonbridge
LDRP 96504	–	–	52913 1985	Peterborough ECD
LDRP 96505	–	–	52914 1985	Millerhill ECD
LDRP 96506	–	–	52915 1985	Heaton ECD
LDRP 96507	–	–	52916 1985	Peterborough ECD
LDRP 96508	–	–	52917 1985	Millerhill ECD
LDRP 96509	–	–	52918 1985	Peterborough ECD
LDRP 96510	–	–	52925 1985	Peterborough ECD
LDRP 96511	–	–	793 1986	Peterborough ECD
LDRP 96512	–	–	52978 1986	Millerhill ECD
LDRP 96513	–	–	52979 1986	Millerhill ECD
LDRP 96514	–	–	52980 1986	Peterborough ECD
–	–	LDB 905034	1971	Peterborough ECD
–	–	LDB 905052	1971	Millerhill ECD
–	–	LDB 905053	1971	Peterborough ECD
–	–	LDB 905056	1971	Millerhill ECD
–	–	LDB 905062	1971	Doncaster Hexthorpe ECD
–	–	LDB 905065	1971	Heaton ECD

Note: During 1991 and the first half of 1992 a significant number of the vehicles detailed above will be based at Kings Norton ECD for use on the electrification of Birmingham's Cross-City line.

M & EE Diesel Hydraulic Breakdown Crane

Current Stock:

ADRC 96700	ADB 967160	–	87 1961	Thornaby
ADRC 96701	ADB 966111	–	78 1961	Stratford
ADRC 96702	ADB 966112	–	79 1961	Toton
ADRC 96703	–	RS 1093/75	81 1961	Wimbledon
ADRC 96704	–	ADB 365	82 1961	Tinsley
ADRC 96705	–	RS 1075/75	83 1961	Doncaster
ADRC 96706	–	RS 1092/75	80 1961	Chart Leacon
ADRC 96707	–	ADB 141	85 1961	Eastleigh
ADRC 96708	–	RS 1095/75	84 1961	Tyseley
ADRC 96709	ADB 967159	–	86 1961	Ashford Crane Repair Depot
ADRC 96710	ADB 966089	–	31146 1977	Crewe
ADRC 96711	ADB 966090	–	31150 1977	Haymarket
ADRC 96712	ADB 966091	–	31147 1977	Old Oak Common

ADRC 96713	ADB 966092	–		31148 1977	Crewe
ADRC 96714	ADB 966093	–		31149 1977	Cardiff
ADRC 96715	ADB 966094	–		31145 1977	Carlisle Upperby
ADRC 96716	–	ADE 331156		6872 1939	Ashford Crane Repair Depot
ADRC 96717	–	RS 1058/45		6870 1939	Motherwell
ADRC 96718	–	RS 1085/45		8053 1953	Laira
ADRC 96719	–	ADE 330110		6871 1939	Brighton
ADRC 96720	–	ADE 330133		6873 1939	Stewarts Lane (SR relief crane)

S & T General Material Carrier with Hoist

Current Stock:

(KDRB 96800)	–	KDM 720905	–	1969	Chester
–	–	KDB 905096	–	–	Chester

MANUAL CRANES

The other grouping of cranes are the manual or hand-cranes of which ten survive. These are mainly used to assist in wagon repairs.

Current Stock:

Number	Previous Identity	Lifting Capacity	Builders	Details	Allocation
Eastern Region					
ADB 967394	–	7½	Taylor and Hubbard	1758 1962	Gateshead OOU
ADB 967397	–	7½	Taylor and Hubbard	1784 1965	Gateshead OOU
London Midland Region					
ADM 47	–	6½	Cowans Sheldon	7571 1942	Shrewsbury Coton Hill OOU
ADM 65	–	6½	Cowans Sheldon	7589 1944	Crewe Gresty Road
Western Region					
060976	ADW 225	6½	Cowans Sheldon	7593 1944	Gloucester
060980	ADW 272	6½	Cowans Sheldon	7588 1944	Hereford
060986	ADW 224	6½	Cowans Sheldon	7215 1941	Swindon RCE Stores
061014	ADS 2008	6½	Cowans Sheldon	8512 1944	Exmouth Jn.
061023	ADW 226	6½	Cowans Sheldon	7577 1944	Cardiff Canton OOU
Southern Region					
083332	ADS 1854	6½	Cowans Sheldon	8334 1945	Tonbridge

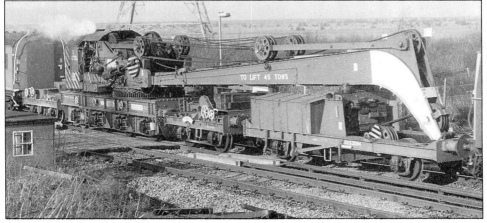

The last two steam breakdown cranes to survive on British Rail were ADRR 95209/10. The former is pictured in steam at Hoo Jn. on 30th January 1985.   Bob Wallace

SMALL PLANT

In complete contrast to the large track maintenance machines, there has in recent years been an expanding use of smaller plant for 'spot' maintenance. This plant is the mechanical equivalent of the work-gang in terms of possession required, the distinctive characteristic being that they reach the worksite by road as far as possible and occupy the track only while actually working.

There are two basic design philosophies applied to these off-track machines. One is to have the equipment fitted to a lorry and equipped with a set of rail wheels. The other is to have a rail vehicle light enough to be carried in a small lorry and able to be lifted on and off the track.

This section is therefore divided into the above two categories, the road/rail vehicles being detailed first. In addition to those road/rail vehicles detailed below reference should be made to DX 68812/3 and DX 68901–8, details of which can be found in the section on 68XXX personnel carriers. The second category of machines moved to and from site by lorry is in two groups, the first one being machines which only have regional numbers, whilst the second group is those machines centrally numbered.

Bruff Tractor Road/Rail Flail Unit (Hedgetrimmer)

Lineside vegetation clearance on British Rail has been made more effective by the use of specially adapted road/rail mowing machines.
British Rail have purchased their own fleet of such machines and eight are in stock. Only the vehicles owned by British Rail are detailed below.

Current Stock:

Regional Identity	Registration	Allocation
05001	OHY 308Y	Southern Central
05002	OHY 309Y	Southern SE
05003	OHY 310Y	Southern Central
05604	A685 PYD	Bristol
05026	A686 PYD	Watford/Birmingham
05606	A687 PYD	Norwich
05607	A668 PYD	Preston/Manchester/Merseyside/Crewe
05608	B240 LNN	Nottingham

Note: 05002/3 have been converted to woodchippers, whilst 05607 has had its flail unit replaced by a shredder.

Bruff Road/Rail Breakdown Unit

The Bruff is a vehicle which can travel to a railway incident either by road or rail and provide all the men, equipment and power required in most cases to get the trains running again, and then get itself out of the way quickly. Along roads it is driven as a normal medium sized 2-wheel drive truck. For cross country use the large road wheels and 4-wheel drive enable the roughest terrain to be crossed. When the rail line is reached the Bruff crosses the tracks and is raised on the turntable. One man turns the vehicle until it is in line with the rails, the rail wheels are then lowered and the turntable retracted. Equipment carried includes jacks, cutting gear, flood and spot working lights. The vehicle is based on a Bedford chassis.

Current Stock:

Registration	Builders Number	Allocation
B155 VRV	501	Colchester
B445 WPO	502	Laira
B534 WTP	504	Toton
B849 XOR	503	Old Oak Common
C921 YOR	507	Allerton
C922 YOR	508	Reading
C923 YOR	510	Immingham
C929 YOR	511	Crewe
C948 YOR	521	Holyhead
C951 YOR	520	Doncaster
C952 YOR	506	Haymarket
C953 YOR	505	Thornaby
C954 YOR	512	Knottingley

C955 YOR	514	Cardiff Canton
C956 YOR	513	Carlisle Upperby
C957 YOR	515	Stratford
C958 YOR	516	Bletchley
C959 YOR	517	Inverness
C960 YOR	519	Tyseley
C961 YOR	518	Gateshead
C962 YOR	529	Longsight
C963 YOR	530	Norwich
C964 YOR	522	Hornsey
C965 YOR	523	Willesden
C966 YOR	524	Cambridge
C967 YOR	525	Motherwell
C968 YOR	526	Ashford
C969 YOR	527	Eastleigh
C970 YOR	528	Brighton
C997 XPX	509	Eastfield

Matisa Road/Rail Tamper

Mounted on a Ford truck chassis, the Matisa road/rail tamper weighs just over ten tons and has a hydraulically-operated turntable enabling it to be lifted clear of the ground and swung manually into position above the rails.

By road, it can travel to the nearest rail access point at a top speed of 50 mph, whilst on track its top speed is just under 20 mph. The power for all functions comes from the 6.2 litre Ford diesel engine and when working the tamper does 3200 vibrations a minute and has a slewing capacity of 4½ inches either way.

This is the second use of this number series (see track machines section).

Current Stock:

Number	Registration	Builders Details	Allocation
74200	PVS 145W	280 1980	Rutherglen OOU

Zweiweg Road/Rail Breakdown Unit

Initially two Zweiweg vehicles were leased to British Rail for evaluation. However the order was placed with Bruff (see above), whose Road/Rail Breakdown Unit is rather larger. KYH 862X has now been converted to a Road/Rail Track Welding Unit (see DX 68812), whilst DWU 335Y is currently being used as a spare to the Bruff fleet. Both vehicles are now owned by British Rail.

Current Stock:

Registration	Allocation
DWU 335Y	Perth

Geismar Road/Rail G.85 Loader/Excavator

These machines can be used for loading and handling operations, earth moving, brush clearing and demolition. On the road they can travel at 19 mph, whilst on track their top speed is 22 mph. On and off tracking can be achieved by its own means in a few seconds.

Current Stock:

Number	Registration	Builders Details	Allocation
09101	D167 VNN	G.85 4207 1986	Reading
09009	E22 LBT	G.85 4208 1988	Leeds

BR Road/Rail Excavator

This one-off conversion is owned by the D of M & EE and is an Atlas 150 'Rocket' 1302 DK wheeled hydraulic excavator with road/rail conversion gear added. It is mainly used for digging out catenary foundations.

Current Stock:

Registration	Allocation
OHS 167V	Heaton ECD

Bruff Road/Rail Access Vehicle

This vehicle was initially supplied to the D of M & EE in 1987 for trial purposes and was fitted with a scissor lift platform. The vehicle was subsequently purchased for development purposes and was fitted with demountable tanks for moving carriage cleaning materials to sites where there is no road access. The next equipment to be fitted on this vehicle was a Simon Topper platform. The demountable tanks are to be fitted on again for its next task.

Current Stock:

Registration	Current Location
D802 CTP	Armthorpe Motors, Doncaster (pending allocation to Reading)

Bruff Road/Rail Overhead Inspection and Traction Unit

This vehicle performs the dual function of being able to shunt tunnel inspection wagons into position, whilst also carrying a Zipper power platform on its back, which is itself used to carry out tunnel inspection duties.

Current Stock:

Number	Registration	Allocation
14201	F621 PWP	Bristol Ashton Gate

Midequip Road/Rail Self-Loading Concrete Mixer

This vehicle has been built in conjunction with Messersi of Italy and will be particularly useful for small scale instalations of electrification mast foundations and maintenance work requiring concrete. It is equipped with a diesel powered hydrostatic transmission system to give excellent rough terrain capabilities.

Registration	Allocation
H926 DRY	Millerhill ECD

Note: To be transferred to Peterborough ECD during 1991.

Permaquip Road/Rail Tunnel Cleaner/Sweeper

This vehicle is a variant of the 3.5 tonne GVW general purpose vehicle marketed by this manufacturer. Equipped with the Fairmont Hy-Rail guidance system, it is for use in the Stansted Airport tunnel link.

Current Stock:

Registration	Allocation
–	Cambridge

Permaquip Road/Rail Emergency Overhead Line Vehicle

This vehicle is a 17-tonne GVW Iveco-Magirus equipped with crane and bucket lift and overhead line drum carrying capability. It is equipped with the Fairmont Hy-Rail guidance system and is to be used as an incident response vehicle on the Anglia Region. It is due to be delivered early in 1991.

Current Stock:

Registration	Allocation
–	Romford OHLM

Permaquip Road/Rail Hy-Lift Overhead Line Access Vehicle

This vehicle is a variant of the 3.5 tonne GVW general purpose vehicle marketed by this manufacturer. Equipped with the Fairmont Hy-Rail guidance system it is capable of being on, off or cross-tracked in almost any circumstances by the driver alone.

Registration	Allocation
G592 SCH	Doncaster OHLM

Geismar MRT-2 Sleeper Changer

These machines remove and insert sleepers and are capable of changing 55 sleepers per hour. They are powered by a diesel engine and have two retractable tyres for on or off-tracking. They are capable of travelling at 25 mph and the operator is protected from the elements by a canvas canopy.

Both the Southern Region and Western Region machines are recorded by their respective regions as 30003, but centrally the Southern Region machine is recorded as 30002.

As regards allocation the Sleeper Changers generally work wherever required on their region, although for maintenance purposes they are allocated to the area listed. Only vehicles owned by British Rail are detailed below.

Current Stock:

Number	Builders Details	Allocation
30001	82050 128 1982	Nottingham
30002	84139 152 1984	Southern Central
30003	84012 151 1984	South Wales

Permaquip Panex Clip Extractor

These machines use repeated blows from 10 lb hammers, eight of which are mounted on the periphery of wheels spinning above the lines of clips. This is considered a surer principle of shifting rusted clips than simply pushing them out. Guards shroud the hammer wheels so that the clips are left close to where they are to be reinserted. The machine removes two lines of clips in one direction, turns around on its central turntable and removes the other two lines on the return trip.

The clip driving mechanism consists of four hydraulically powered arms which operate simultaneously. The contoured heads fit over the rounds of the clips, which have previously been hand placed. The driver positions the machine over each sleeper before operating the hydraulic mechanism and the reaction from the four motions cancel out so that there is little load on the brakes.

The existing fleet are all Mk 2, but the delivery of the Permaclippers which extract and insert rail fasteners means that only one machine is still being used.

Current Stock:

Regional Identity	Builders Details	Allocation
54/140	203 1979	Newcastle Forth Bank OOU
54/187	205 1980	Norwich
54951	206 1980	Kilmarnock OOU

Pandrol Pandriver Clip Installers

These machines drive Pandrol rail clips into sleeper fasteners. Pandrol market various types, the most modern being the Mark 6. All the examples on British Rail are Mark 3. The purchase of these machines took place at the same time as the Permaquip Panex Clip extractor, but the delivery of the Permaclippers which extract and insert rail fasteners means that all these machines are awaiting disposal.

No all region number series has been allocated, and consequently they are listed under builders number order.

Current Stock:

Regional Identity	Builders Details	Allocation
54/197	3000 1978	Crofton OOU
54950	3004 1978	Kilmarnock OOU
54/190	3033 1980	York Leeman Road OOU
54/192	3035 1980	Newcastle Forth Bank OOU
54/194	3037 1980	Norwich OOU

UHL Panclipper

This machine performs the same functions as a Permaclipper and is the only one of its type on British Rail.

Current Stock:

Regional Identity	Builders Details	Allocation
54287	— 1986	Crewe

Plasser and Theurer HGR 230 Lifter and Slewer

These are small four-wheeled vehicles which are self-propelled and move along the track at walking pace. The HGR 230 has hydraulically-operated vertical thrusters extending from booms on either side. When the appropriate control is selected two heavy clamps grip the rails, the thrusters emerge and both vehicle and track are pushed upwards. Using this machine, one man can lift a sixty foot panel of track and slew it as much as ten inches.

No all-region number series has been issued, and machines are therefore listed in builders number order. The machines are all of the 2-RZ type. Only 14 of the 40 machines purchased in 1976 survive.

A number have been resold for use on preserved lines including 14/25/6/31/40 to the Midland Railway Centre, Butterley.

Current Stock:

Regional Identity	Builders Details	Allocation
56201	3 1976	Scottish NE
62001 & SR 6463	7 1976	Southern SE
62216	11 1976	Kilmarnock OOU
62003 & SR 6502	15 1976	Southern SE
60124 & PWM 8783	16 1976	Reading
62208	17 1976	Scottish NE
60125 & PWM 8784	19 1976	South Wales
60126 & PWM 8785	21 1976	Exeter
62211	23 1976	Scottish NE
62207	28 1976	Scottish NE
60127 & PWM 8786	32 1976	South Wales
60128 & PWM 8787	33 1976	South Wales
60130 & PWM 8789	35 1976	South Wales
60133 & PWM 8792	39 1976	Exeter

Geismar Lifter and Slewer

These machines perform the same function as the Plasser and Theurer HGR 230 Lifter and Slewer, and two examples survive in Scotland.

Current Stock:

Regional Identity	Builders Details	Allocation
62204	75002 102 1975	Kilmarnock OOU
62206	76065 105 1976	Kilmarnock OOU

Permaquip Powered Muscleman

These machines are designed to lift and slew concrete and timber sleepered track and to lift and hold track for manual packing. Power is provided by an air cooled petrol engine. The Muscleman comprises three main assemblies, the power pack, base frame and main frame. These three assemblies are readily separated for portability. A turntable is also supplied as a standard part of the base frame, thus allowing the complete machine to be on/off tracked by two men.

Only machines with ride-on facilities are included in this book and the six Muscleman machines purchased by the London Midland Region at the end of 1987 are all so equipped.

Current Stock:

Number	Builders Details	Allocation
	Q124 1987	Crewe
56084	Q125 1987	Manchester
56085	Q126 1987	Preston
56060	Q127 1987	Nottingham
56061	Q128 1987	Birmingham
56062	Q129 1987	Birmingham

Permaquip Rastic and Superlev

This pair of machines was developed in conjunction with British Rail's Derby Research and Development Division and are designed to correct dips at welded rail joints. These dips can be the source of as much as 25% of track roughness and track geometry deteriorates more rapidly as roughness increases. Faster and more cost effective than existing machines the rail straightening machine – known as Rastic – can control the rail bending operation so that the vertical rail geometry at the weld is restored accurately and quickly.

In order that a straightened rail does not bend again at the weld, a second machine called the Superlev mills a smooth running surface on the rail before the sleepers around the weld are packed in the conventional way. Both machines are compatible with tamping machines, allowing correction of weld geometry to be carried out in the same track possession.

The Superlev has been purchased by British Rail, whilst the Rastic is still under evaluation.

Current Stock: – Superlev

Number	Builders Details	Allocation
–	001 1985	Derby Technical Centre

Current Stock: – Rastic

Number	Builders Details	Allocation
86201	001 1985	Derby Technical Centre

Permaquip Platform Lift

These machines are designed to permit easy access to bridges, tunnels and overhead electrification equipment for inspection, maintenance, installation or conversion. Weight is under 3 tonnes and the Platform Lift can be moved quickly on and off the track. Initially the standard power unit was a 10 hp diesel engine, but from machine PL025 standard fitting has been a 20 hp diesel engine which is capable of a speed of 15 mph when the platform is down. The inspection platform is fully protected to meet all safety requirements and is raised by a scissor jack arrangement. This can be worked to within 1/4 inch levels from just over 4 feet to 18½ feet.

It will be noted that some of the Eastern Region and Scottish Region RCE machines have the same plant numbers. This occurs because each region is responsible for numbering its own machines within either the 14XXX or 54XXX series. The D of M & EE also owns a substantial number of machines, these either being based at an Electrification Construction Depot or an Overhead Line Maintenance Depot. The accompanying table is presented in builders number order.

Current Stock:

Regional Identity	Builders Details	Allocation
– (a)	003 1978	Hornsey OHLM
2559 R	004 1978	Hornsey OHLM OOU
14100	005 1979	RCE Scottish NE
14101	008 1980	RCE Glasgow
14103	011 1980	RCE Glasgow
–	013 1980	Heaton ECD
14102	014 1981	RCE Scottish SE
IT/1	015 1980	Shields Road OOU
14101	016 1981	RCE Leeds
54003	020 1981	Hassocks OOU
14501	021 1981	RCE South Wales
54001	028 1982	RCE Southern SE
14103	030 1983	RCE Doncaster
14102	031 1983	RCE Newcastle
54501	032 1983	RCE Crewe
69113	033 1983	Rugby OHLM
54267	034 1983	RCE Crewe
54500	040 1983	RCE Nottingham
4226 R	041 1983	Romford OHLM
69111	042 1983	Longsight OHLM
4227 R	043 1983	Romford OHLM
69116	044 1983	Longsight OHLM
–	045 1983	Millerhill ECD
–	046 1983	Peterborough ECD
69115	047 1984	Rugby OHLM
–	048 1984	Peterborough ECD
14502	049 1984	RCE South Wales
IT/2	050 1984	Carstairs OHLM
69117	051 1984	Bedford OHLM
14104	056 1984	RCE Leeds

Only two of the twenty-eight Permaquip High Capacity Overhead Work Trolleys are owned by the civil engineer. One of them is 14104 (wrongly numbered 04104), pictured here at Rutherglen Training Centre on 13th May 1988.　　　　　　　　　　　　　　　　　Bob Wallace

Permaquip ballast packer 74029 is seen awaiting to be used at Pirton on 17th January 1988.
Stephen Widdowson

IT/3	057 1984	Shields OHLM
4588 R	058 1984	Cheshunt OHLM
4589 R	059 1984	Pitsea OHLM
–	060 1984	Colchester OHLM
–	061 1984	Romford OHLM
–	062 1985	Romford OHLM
–	063 1985	Colchester OHLM
54284	064 1985	RCE Manchester
–	065 1985	Heaton ECD
–	066 1985	Peterborough ECD
–	067 1985	Peterborough ECD
–	068 1985	Millerhill ECD
–	069 1985	Peterborough ECD
–	070 1985	Millerhill ECD
69114	071 1987	Bletchley OHLM
69112	072 1987	Willesden OHLM
–	074 1988	Pitsea OHLM
–	075 1988	Cheshunt OHLM

(a) frame is a trailer for HCT 027.

Permaquip High Capacity Overhead Work Trolley

A prototype, known as the OLEV, was built in 1986 using a BREV chassis and the scissor-lift off hire machine PL012. Following its use on the Anglian electrification scheme British Rail acquired five production HCTs in 1986/7. So successful have these machines proved that a further sixteen were ordered, delivery to take place during 1988.

This was followed by a further order in 1988 for one machine for the civil engineer and an additional six in 1989 for the OHLM engineer. 029–031 were sold in 1990 to the contractor Siemens for use in Spain.

The HCT provides a safe means of working at heights above the track and outreaches from the track. It is a fully self-contained unit with ample lighting and power take-off points. The diesel engine can be stopped (and re-started) from the platform allowing quiet and fumeless working conditions. The HCT can be off-tracked and stabled alongside the worksite between track possessions. For the civil engineer the HCT can be used for the inspection, maintenance and repair of tunnels and bridges, whilst for the OHLM engineer it is used to install, inspect and maintain overhead lines.

Current Stock:

Number	Builders Details	Allocation
–	001 1986	Carstairs OHLM
–	002 1987	Hornsey OHLM
14104	003 1987	RCE Muirhouse
–	004 1987	Peterborough OHLM
–	005 1987	Romford OHLM (Minor New Works)
69100	006 1988	Crewe OHLM
69101	007 1988	Rugby OHLM
–	008 1988	Romford OHLM (Minor New Works)
–	009 1988	Peterborough OHLM
–	010 1988	Morpeth OHLM
–	011 1988	Carstairs OHLM
–	012 1988	Doncaster OHLM
–	013 1988	Carstairs OHLM
69102	014 1988	Bletchley OHLM
69103	015 1988	Bletchley OHLM
69104	016 1988	Soho OHLM
69105	017 1988	Stafford OHLM
69106	018 1988	Willesden OHLM
69107	019 1988	Longsight OHLM
–	020 1988	Carstairs OHLM (for Portobello OHLM)
–	021 1988	Carstairs OHLM (for Portobello OHLM)
14105	022 1988	RCE Southern Central
69108	023 1989	Soho OHLM
–	024 1989	Morpeth OHLM
69109	025 1989	Wigan OHLM
69110	026 1989	Crewe OHLM

Permaquip Ballast Packer

This machine uses a pincer motion to pack ballast with eight hydraulically-powered independent packing arms, each having a packing force of 1.2 tonnes. This pincer action is claimed to avoid unnecessary sleeper-bay disturbance and also compacts ballast to a lower level. It is self-powered with its own 30 hp diesel engine which drives the hydraulic system and can also propel the ballast packer at 10 mph along the track. It is transported to the work site by road in a standard 3 tonne lorry. The Ballast Packer is equipped with its own hydraulic lifting turntable which can lift it onto the rails, or transfer it between tracks, in four minutes.

The Mk 5 Ballast Packer is fitted with a fully enclosed and heated cab and adjustable track lift rams and a programme of similarly improving the Mk 3 and Mk 4 versions has taken place.

The 74XXX number series is used for these machines, this being the second use of this series (see track machine section). However as will be seen from the accompanying table the London Midland Region originally considered that the 54XXX series (miscellaneous self-powered plant) was more appropriate. The other anomoly is that the Eastern Region used 74092–9 as temporary 74XXX numbers for the eight ballast packers it initially hired before purchasing. The numbers 74048/9 were not issued. 74071 was previously numbered 74061 and initially 74000.

As regards allocation, these machines are listed on the same basis as the large track maintenance machines. Only machines owned by British Rail are detailed below.

Current Stock:

Number	Regional Identity	Type	Builders Details	Allocation
74001	–	Mk 3	006 1980	Newcastle
74002	–	Mk 3	007 1981	Norwich
74003	–	Mk 3	008 1981	Peterborough
74004	–	Mk 3	009 1981	Leeds
74006	–	Mk 3	011 1981	Newcastle
74007	–	Mk 3	012 1981	Doncaster
74008	–	Mk 3	013 1981	Peterborough
74009	–	Mk 3	014 1981	Doncaster
74010	–	Mk 4	015 1981	Glasgow
74011	–	Mk 4	016 1981	Scottish NE
74012	54301	Mk 4	018 1982	Nottingham
74013	54302	Mk 4	019 1982	Watford
74014	54303	Mk 4	020 1982	Watford
74015	54304	Mk 4	021 1982	Preston
74016	74093	Mk 4	022 1983	Doncaster
74017	74094	Mk 4	024 1983	Newcastle
74018	74095	Mk 4	025 1983	Leeds
74019	74096	Mk 4	026 1983	Norwich
74020	74097	Mk 4	027 1983	Leeds
74021	74099	Mk 4	028 1983	Peterborough
74022	74092	Mk 4	029 1983	Newcastle
74023	74098	Mk 4	030 1983	Peterborough
74024	54305	Mk 4	031 1982	Manchester/Merseyside
74025	54307	Mk 4	032 1982	Birmingham
74026	54309	Mk 4	033 1982	Manchester/Merseyside
74027	–	Mk 4	034 1983	Scottish SE
74028	–	Mk 4	023 1983	Scottish SE
74029	–	Mk 4	035 1983	Bristol
74030	–	Mk 4	036 1983	Reading
74031	–	Mk 4	037 1983	Exeter
74032	–	Mk 4	038 1983	York Leeman Road OOU
			(rebuild of 017 1981)	
74033	–	Mk 4	039 1983	Exeter
74034	–	Mk 4	040 1983	Bristol
74035	–	Mk 4	041 1983	South Wales
74036	–	Mk 4	042 1983	South Wales
74037	54306	Mk 4	043 1983	Watford

Tamper Tracgopher 76001 is photographed at Ashford on 9th July 1988.   Bob Wallace

Permaquip Permaclipper 51634 is pictured at Lenton on 9th August 1986.   Gary Grafton

74038	54308	Mk 4	044 1983	Birmingham
74039	54311	Mk 4	045 1983	Crewe
74040	54312	Mk 4	046 1983	Crewe
74041	54310	Mk 4	047 1983	Preston
74042	54315	Mk 4	048 1983	Nottingham
74043	54313	Mk 4	055 1983	Crewe
74044	–	Mk 4	051 1983	Scottish NE
74045	–	Mk 4	052 1983	Scottish SE
74046	–	Mk 4	053 1983	Glasgow
74047	–	Mk 4	054 1983	Scottish SE
74050	–	Mk 4	049 1983	South Wales
74051	–	Mk 4	050 1983	South Wales
74052	–	Mk 4	056 1983	Peterborough
74053	–	Mk 4	057 1983	York Leeman Road OOU
74054	–	Mk 4A	058 1984	South Wales
74055	–	Mk 4A	059 1984	Glasgow
74056	–	Mk 5	060 1984	Glasgow
74057	–	Mk 5	061 1984	Scottish SE
74058	–	Mk 5	062 1984	Exeter
74059	–	Mk 5	063 1984	Bristol
74060	–	Mk 5	064 1984	Reading
74061	–	Mk 5	068 1988	Nottingham
74071	–	Mk 3	005 1980	Doncaster

Plasser and Theurer Minima II Tamper

The Minima II is a small tamping machine with a lifting and slewing device for mechanised maintenance of small sites and for use behind ballast cleaning machines, or after track renewal work. The two tamping units with a total of eight tamping tines can be lowered and squeezed independently from one another. The lifting and slewing device is positioned directly in front of the tamping units. The track is lifted by means of two rail clamps gripping on the rail head and hydraulic cylinders which are supported on the ballast bed between the sleeper ends. A horizontal hydraulic cylinder mounted on the supports permits the track to be slewed, whilst a track superelevation gauge serves to check the track cross level.

This is the second use of this number series (see track machines section).

Current Stock:

CEPS Number	Builders Details	Allocation
74100	22 1978	Scottish NE

Tamper GO4 Tracgopher

These machines are shoulder and six-foot ballast cleaners. They have a four wheel drive and are used for digging trenches for laying pipe and signal cable, lowering track in bridges and tunnels for clearance purposes, undercutting approaches to bridges and clearing debris and foul ballast between double tracks.

The digging wheel cuts parallel to the track, adjacent to the tie ends. As the trench is cut, the undercutter bar cuts underneath the track, discharging the foul ballast into the trench. The scarifier buckets mounted on the digging wheel pick up the ballast and deposit on the digging wheel conveyor. The operator will have pre-set the duration of movement on the digging wheel conveyor before operations began. When extended the ballast runs through the centre of the digging wheel to the trench side of the track. When retracted the ballast runs onto the swing conveyor.

Although the 760XX number series is used for these machines, this being the second use of this series (see track machine section), the London Midland Region also initially allocated its own regional identity. 76003 was originally numbered 76000. Only machines owned by British Rail are detailed below. For 76004 see section on machines available for hire.

Current Stock:

CEPS Number	Regional Identity	Builders Details	Allocation
76001	–	4770046 1978	Southern SE
76002	64000	4780943 1983	Birmingham
76003	–	4780953 1983	York ER HQ

Permaquip Permaclipper

These machines remove and insert rail fasteners at high speed. 002–11 are the Mk 2 version, whilst 012–31 are Mk 3 and 032–41 are Mk 4. The Mk 3 machine has a more spacious cab, now totally enclosed and heated, whilst the engine is more powerful and efficient. The cab and engine cover are hinged for maximum accessibility and ease of servicing. Fail-safe rail hooks and improved lift rams provide speedy rail-jacking, for even the heaviest rail sections.

Initially each region used its own numbering system, but subsequently the 626XX number series was allocated to these machines. However as the 626XX series was being used by the Western Region for kango hammers,it was first decided to number these machines in the 516XX series. Subsequently the 916XX series was selected. 042–4 have been sold to Finland, Sweden and Belgium respectively.

As regards allocation, the machines are listed on the same basis as the large track maintenance machines.

Current Stock:

Number	Regional Identity	Builders Details	Allocation
91601	–	003 1982	Crewe
91602	–	005 1982	Nottingham
91603	–	009 1982	Birmingham
91604	–	008 1982	Crewe
91605	–	011 1983	Newcastle
91606	–	006 1982	Newcastle
91607	54952	002 1982	Glasgow
91608	54953	010 1983	Scottish SE
91609	14001	007 1982	Reading
91610	14002	004 1982	Bristol
91611	–	012 1984	Leeds
91612	–	015 1984	Peterborough
91613	–	019 1984	Doncaster
91614	–	014 1984	Preston
91615	–	021 1984	Crewe
91616	54954	013 1984	Scottish SE
91617	–	020 1984	South Wales
91618	–	038 1986	Peterborough
91619	–	022 1984	Southern SE
91620	–	023 1985	Southern SE
91621	54955	016 1984	Scottish NE
91622	–	018 1984	Glasgow
91623	–	026 1985	Exeter
91624	–	025 1985	Scottish SE
91625	–	027 1985	Nottingham
91626	–	024 1985	Preston
91627	–	028 1985	South Wales
91628	–	029 1985	Scottish NE
91629	–	031 1985	Crewe
91630	–	030 1985	Manchester/Merseyside
91631	–	032 1986	Doncaster
91632	–	033 1986	Manchester/Merseyside
91633	–	034 1986	Doncaster
91634	–	035 1986	Nottingham
91635	–	036 1986	Stratford
91636	–	037 1986	Norwich
91637	–	017 1984	Southern Central
91638	–	039 1986	Exeter
91639	–	040 1986	Southern SW
91640	–	041 1987	Leeds

Note: During the renumbering of these machines 91605/6 have swopped identity as have 91618/ 37. The 'new' 91618 has yet to be renumbered from 91637, whilst the 'new' 91637 has been renumbered from 91618.

MISCELLANEOUS PLANT

This section is quite simply for those items of on-track plant that do not fall conveniently into any other section of the book, or because of their numbers are best grouped here. For the sake of completeness those wagons which actually work with powered plant ie. the 88XXX Skip Train and the 89XXX LWRT trains are also included. However, the fleet of wagon-mounted equipment numbered in the 63XXX, 64XXX, 65XXX, 66XXX and 67XXX series do not fall within the scope of this book.

82XXX VIADUCT INSPECTION UNIT

These units are not self-propelled needing to be moved by a locomotive. Of the earlier units only DR 82002 survives, whilst the more modern units were a significant advancement. From a stationary position the three man capacity bucket can swoop beneath a bridge to cover an area of some 2,500 square feet. It can even be telescoped right through an arch to allow scrutiny of the unoccupied side of a double track bridge. A single arch can be inspected in less than thirty minutes, including the return and securing of the bucket. The bucket houses all controls plus fan heaters, a radio telephone and powerful lights for night work. An auxillary engine is a standard fitting, in addition to an automatic fail-safe mechanism which ensures that the bucket will not fall or tip in the event of total engine failure.

Unlike the earlier units, no anchor or winch is required on the more modern units and there is no obstruction of adjacent lines when in operation. All the units are built onto wagons, 82001–3 being constructed by British Rail. 82100/1 were built by Elstree Plant and 82201 by Armfield Engineering.

Current Stock:

CEPS Numbers	Additional Identification	Mounted on Wagon	Year Built	Allocation
DR 82002	HP 3/1	DB 996262	1961	Eastern Region
DR 82100	TU 37/1	DM 748349	1975	Southern/Western Regions
DR 82101	TU 37/2	DM 748327	1977	Anglia/Eastern/LM/Scottish Regions
DR 82201	Universal	DB 901202	1980	All Regions (except Scottish)

Vehicles no longer in stock:

DR 82001	–	DB 994001	1961	

Allocated to the Eastern Region. All the equipment except for the cabin was removed at Lowestoft Harbour Works in 1976 and scrapped. The cabin was placed on the ground for use at Lowestoft Harbour Works as a store/office.

DR 82003	HP 3/2	DM 720014	1961	

Allocated to the Scottish Region. Sold from Inverkeithing to the Llangollen Railway 10/88.

Wickham Road/Rail Viaduct Inspection Unit

The vehicle basically consists of a Ford Cargo truck chassis on which is mounted a Topper Underbridge Unit manufactured by Simon-Gala at Thetford. Onto this vehicle are built two retractable rail wheel and axle sets and a turntable for use in transferring the vehicle from road to rail mode and vice versa.

Current Stock:

CEPS Number	Registration	Builders Details	Allocation
82301	G233 BAR	11652 1988	Scottish Region

85XXX TRENCHING UNIT

The first trench-digger was developed by the Western Reion and was driven by a 48 bhp diesel engine, power being transmitted to all motions hydraulically. The traction whilst digging was obtained by a winch winding in a wire rope anchored to the track ahead.

A second trencher was then supplied by Hunslet, a name more normally associated with industrial locomotives, and this second unit is still active. Currently DR 85001 is maintained by the Western Region, but works wherever required on British Rail. It has a locomotive-style driving cab one end and is diesel powered, its works number being 6056.

Current Stock:

	Mounted on Wagon	Year Built	Allocation
DR 85001	DB 965168	1962	Western Region

Vehicle no longer in stock:

DR 85000	DW 100701	1959	

Allocated to the Western Region. Scrapped at Radyr by Phillips (Metals), Llanelli 7/87.

86XXX RAIL JOINT STRAIGHTENER

Of the three machines in this category DX 86001 awaits scrapping, whilst the other two machines DR 86100/1 are used in conjunction with Plasser Rail Grinders DR 79400/1.

Railway Maintenance Corporation Rail Joint Straightener

Current Stock:

DX 86001	DB 965571	RJS 1	3516 1966	Manchester Exchange OOU

Plasser and Theurer Rail Joint Straightener

Current Stock:

DR 86100	–	–	2147 1983	London Midland Region
DR 86101	–	–	2226 1985	Southern Region

Rail Maintenance Corporation Rail Joint Straightner DX 86001 is pictured at Manchester Exchange on 30th August 1987. DX 86001 is the only machine that manufacturer has supplied to British Rail.   Roy Hennefer

88XXX SKIP TRAIN

This train works behind an ordinary ballast cleaning machine and allows the loading of the spoil to be confined to the single track being cleaned. With traditional methods, the spoil train would have to occupy the adjacent line. The train is loaded with dozens of skips which can be carried along its length by travelling gantries working in relay.

The 880XX number series was not used to avoid confusion with the number allocated to the Eastern Region's weedkilling train 88001. The weedkilling train did not however contain any special plant vehicles. DR 88101, DR 88202, and DR 88304 were originally numbered DR 88100, DR 88200 and DR 88300 respectively.

Plasser and Theurer Loading Station

DR 88101	–	–	9635 1981	York ER HQ

Plasser and Theurer Unloading Station

DR 88201	–	No 2	9637 1981	York ER HQ
DR 88202	–	No 1	9636 1981	York ER HQ

Plasser and Theurer Gantry Crane

DR 88301	–	–	9640 1981	York ER HQ
DR 88302	–	–	9639 1981	York ER HQ
DR 88303	–	–	9638 1981	York ER HQ
DR 88304	–	–	9641 1981	York ER HQ

Wagons Included in Skip Train:

DB 997801	DB 997805	DB 997809	DB 997813	DB 997817	DB 997820
DB 997802	DB 997806	DB 997810	DB 997814	DB 997818	DB 997821
DB 997803	DB 997807	DB 997811	DB 997815	DB 997819	DB 997822
DB 997804	DB 997808	DB 997812	DB 997816		

89XXX Long Welded Rail Train

The LWRT is a wagon-mounted handling system which speeds up the laying or lifting of continuous welded rail (CWR). The total train of equipment consists of a power wagon, a rail handling gantry unit which runs on top of the wagons, a stabling wagon with look out/guard cab, a chute wagon with operator's cab, a clamping wagon and eight intermediate wagons.

The power wagon incorporates a diesel engine and is used to drive and brake the train on site during loading and unloading. Thus no locomotive is required. The power wagon is controlled by a single operator who is situated in a cab positioned on the chute wagon. The rail handling gantry unit runs on rails positioned on the outer edges of the wagons, with telescoping bridging pieces spanning the gaps between the wagon ends, thus enabling the gantry unit to travel the length of the train. Powered by its own diesel engine the gantry unit is completely self-contained. The rails are handled by clamps on the end of hydraulically actuated articulated booms projecting from the gantry unit. The chute wagon guides the rails on and off the trackbed whilst the other nine wagons are standard vehicles fitted with roller frames to receive and store the rails. Eight of these wagons are known as intermediate wagons, the other being a clamping wagon for anchoring the rails during transit. The initial order for four trains was placed with Cowans Boyd, but the subsequent further order for twelve more trains was divided equally between Cowans Boyd and Plasser and Theurer.

Current Stock:

Cowans Boyd Power Wagon

DR 89000	–	–	34627 1984	Southern Region
DR 89001	–	–	34628 1984	Eastern Region
DR 89002	–	–	34629 1984	Eastern Region
DR 89003	–	–	34630 1984	London Midland Region
DR 89004	–	–	34972 1985	Scottish Region
DR 89005	–	–	34973 1985	London Midland Region
DR 89006	–	–	34974 1985	London Midland Region
DR 89007	–	–	34975 1985	London Midland Region
DR 89008	–	–	34976 1985	London Midland Region
DR 89009	–	–	34977 1985	Eastern Region

Plasser and Theurer Power Wagon

DR 89010	–	–	52801 1985	Western Region
DR 89011	–	–	52811 1985	Southern Region
DR 89012	–	–	52821 1985	Western Region
DR 89013	–	–	52831 1985	Southern Region
DR 89014	–	–	52841 1985	Southern Region
DR 89015	–	–	52851 1985	Southern Region

Cowans Boyd Gantry Unit

	Mounted on Stabling Wagon		
DR 89100	DB 979600	33699 1982	Southern Region
DR 89101	DB 979601	34586 1983	Eastern Region
DR 89102	DB 979602	34557 1983	Eastern Region
DR 89103	DB 979603	34558 1983	London Midland Region
DR 89104	DB 979604	34995 1985	Scottish Region
DR 89105	DB 979605	34996 1985	London Midland Region
DR 89106	DB 979606	34997 1985	London Midland Region
DR 89107	DB 979607	34998 1985	London Midland Region
DR 89108	DB 979608	34999 1985	London Midland Region
DR 89109	DB 979609	35000 1985	Eastern Region

Note: Cowans Boyd allocated builders numbers 35007–12 to DB 979604–9 respectively and 35019–24 to the lookout cabin on the stabling wagon. No separate builders numbers were issued for DB 979600–3 and their lookout cabins.

Plasser and Theurer Gantry Unit

	Mounted on Stabling Wagon		
DR 89110	DB 979610	635 1985	Western Region
DR 89111	DB 979611	636 1985	Southern Region
DR 89112	DB 979612	52825 1985	Western Region
DR 89113	DB 979613	52835 1985	Southern Region
DR 89114	DB 979614	52845 1985	Southern Region
DR 89115	DB 979615	52855 1985	Southern Region

Note: Plasser allocated builders numbers 52804/14/24/34/44/54 to DB 979610–5 respectively.

Cowans Boyd Chute Wagon

	Mounted on Wagon			
DR 89200	DB 979500	34899	1984	Southern Region
DR 89201	DB 979501	34900	1984	Eastern Region
DR 89202	DB 979502	34901	1984	Eastern Region
DR 89203	DB 979503	34902	1984	London Midland Region
DR 89204	DB 979504	35001/13 1985		Scottish Region
DR 89205	DB 979505	35002/14 1985		London Midland Region
DR 89206	DB 979506	35003/15 1985		London Midland Region
DR 89207	DB 979507	35004/16 1985		London Midland Region
DR 89208	DB 979508	35005/17 1985		London Midland Region
DR 89209	DB 979509	35006/18 1985		Eastern Region

Note: Cowans Boyd allocated builders numbers 35001–6 to Chute wagons DB 979504–9 respectively and 35013–8 to the operator's cab on DB 979504–9 respectively. No separate builders numbers were issued for DB 979500–3 and their operator's cabs.

Plasser and Theurer Chute Wagon

	Mounted on Wagon		
DR 89210	DB 979510	52800 1985	Western Region
DR 89211	DB 979511	52810 1985	Southern Region

DR 89212	DB 979512	52820 1985	Western Region
DR 89213	DB 979513	52830 1985	Southern Region
DR 89214	DB 979514	52840 1985	Southern Region
DR 89215	DB 979515	52850 1985	Southern Region

Other Wagons included in CWR Trains
Clamping Wagons:

Number Now Allocated	Number Actually Carried	Original Number
DB 979400	DB 979025	DB 979025
DB 979401	DB 979004	DB 979004
DB 979402	DB 979031	DB 979031
DB 979403	DB 979011	DB 979011
DB 979404	DB 979400	DB 979400
DB 979405	DB 979401	DB 979401
DB 979406	DB 979408	DB 979402
DB 979407	DB 979403	DB 979403
DB 979408	DB 979404	DB 979404
DB 979409	DB 979409	DB 979405
DB 979410	DB 979410	DB 979406
DB 979411	DB 979411	DB 979407
DB 979412	DB 979412	DB 979408
DB 979413	DB 979413	DB 979409
DB 979414	DB 979414	DB 979410
DB 979415	DB 979415	DB 979411

Notes:

(1) For planning of loading, movement and maintenance purposes it was decided in February 1986 that for all sixteen trains the Power Wagon, Gantry Crane and Stabling Wagon, Chute Wagon and Clamping Wagon should all share the last two numbers.

(2) A renumbering of the original numbers carried by the Clamping Wagons was therefore authorised, but as will be seen by the above table it was never fully implemented.

(3) As DB 979402 was renumbered DB 979408, DB 979404 will now need to be renumbered DB 979406 should it be decided to fully implement the renumbering scheme.

(4) Plasser builders numbers for DB 979410–15 are 52803/13/23/33/43/53 respectively.

Intermediate Wagons:

DB 979000	DB 979024	DB 979048	DB 979069	DB 979090	DB 979111
DB 979001	DB 979026	DB 979049	DB 979070	DB 979091	DB 979112
DB 979002	DB 979027	DB 979050	DB 979071	DB 979092	DB 979113
DB 979003	DB 979028	DB 979051	DB 979072	DB 979093	DB 979114
DB 979005	DB 979029	DB 979052	DB 979073	DB 979094	DB 979115
DB 979006	DB 979030	DB 979053	DB 979074	DB 979095	DB 979116
DB 979007	DB 979032	DB 979054	DB 979075	DB 979096	DB 979117
DB 979008	DB 979033	DB 979055	DB 979076	DB 979097	DB 979118
DB 979009	DB 979034	DB 979056	DB 979077	DB 979098	DB 979119
DB 979010	DB 979035	DB 979057	DB 979078	DB 979099	DB 979120
DB 979012	DB 979036	DB 979058	DB 979079	DB 979100	DB 979121
DB 979013	DB 979037	DB 979059	DB 979080	DB 979101	DB 979122
DB 979014	DB 979038	DB 979060	DB 979081	DB 979102	DB 979123
DB 979015	DB 979039	DB 979061	DB 979082	DB 979103	DB 979124
DB 979016	DB 979040	DB 979062	DB 979083	DB 979104	DB 979125
DB 979017	DB 979041	DB 979063	DB 979084	DB 979105	DB 979126
DB 979018	DB 979042	DB 979064	DB 979085	DB 979106	DB 979127
DB 979019	DB 979043	DB 979065	DB 979086	DB 979107	DB 979128
DB 979020	DB 979044	DB 979066	DB 979087	DB 979108	DB 979129
DB 979021	DB 979045	DB 979067	DB 979088	DB 979109	DB 979130
DB 979022	DB 979046	DB 979068	DB 979089	DB 979110	DB 979131
DB 979023	DB 979047				

Notes:

(1) The above list consists of 128 wagons (8 intermediate wagons to each train)

(2) Plasser allocated builders numbers 52802/12/22/32/42/52 to each set of eight wagons e.g DB 979084–91 are 52802 (1–8) respectively, DB 979092–99 are 52812 (1–8) respectively etc.

(3) DB 979004/11/25/31 are not included in the above list as they are actually clamping wagons (see above).

931XX LINERCRANE

This number series is not part of the CEPS scheme, but is included as it is a self-propelled vehicle. F93100 was built by Ralph Blatchford, Midsomer Norton and is a road/rail container transfer crane and can be used wherever there are two parallel rail tracks. It is powered by a 150 hp Rolls-Royce diesel engine and can shunt a five-car set of Freightliner wagons when required. It is capable of lifting 20, 30 or 40 ft ISO containers and transferring them to road or rail vehicles.

Current Stock:

Number	Builders Details	Allocation
F93100	S1030 1984	Willesden FLT

94XXX SLEEPER SQUARER

Only three machines fall in this category, DX 94416 having been converted by BR from Plasser 06-32 Tamper DX 74416. DX 94501 is a purpose-built self-propelled machine built by Permaquip and can square sleepers in a single operation without digging out ballast beds, unclipping rail or disturbing the track. Sleepers can also be spaced or re-spaced. DX 94501 can be on and off-tracked using the Permaquip Tracess system, and has a spare cab originally intended for Permaclipper 012. DX 94600 was built by Tamper (Australia) and is a self-propelled machine for spacing, re-spacing or resquaring sleepers.

Plasser and Theurer Sleeper Squarer

Vehicle no longer in stock:

DX 94416   DB 965718   DTM 21   688 1968

See DX 74416 for historical details.

Permaquip Sleeper Squarer

Current Stock:

DX 94501   –   –   001 1985   Reading

Tamper CSS Sleeper Squarer

Current Stock:

DX 94600   –   –   926230 1990   Preston

Shunting Locomotives (Conversions from Ballast Cleaners)

Current Stock:

97601	ex DR 76105	Slateford
97602	ex DR 76212	Kilmarnock
97603	ex DR 76104	Slateford

Note:

Although recorded centrally as 97601–3 (to avoid duplicate numbers) these three 'locomotives' are actually numbered 97701–3 respectively, thus duplicating the numbers of the D of M & EE's battery locomotives.

SNOWPLOUGHS

Current Stock:

Tender Mounted Large Plough

ADE 979	Norwich	DE 330966	SB	ADE 330982	SB

Large Plough with Guards Compartment

ADB 981	TY	ADB 985	GD	ADB 990	Norwich
ADB 982	TY	ADB 986	GD	ADB 991	Holbeck
ADB 983	GD	ADB 987	TE	ADB 992	Holbeck
ADB 984	GD	ADB 988	TE		

Wagon-mounted Snowblower

69001 on DB 991559   Perth
69002 on DB 991482   Kilmarnock (conversion uncompleted)

Tender Mounted Medium Plough

ADE 330964	DR	ADE 330970	MR	ADE 330977	CR
ADE 330968	CR	ADE 330976	MR		

Tender Mounted Plough (Former 'Schools' Class)

ADS 70210	Ashford	ADS 70225	EH OOU	ADS 70228	SU
ADS 70211	Ashford	(for Bluebell Rly)		ADS 70229	EH
ADS 70224	EH OOU	ADS 70227	SU		
(for Swanage Rly)					

Tender Mounted Plough

ADB 965189   BS

BR Standard Independent Plough

ADB 965196	CD	ADB 965217	FW	ADB 965232	BR
ADB 965197	PH	ADB 965218	Carlisle	ADB 965233	BR
ADB 965198	CD	ADB 965219	PH	ADB 965234	IS
ADB 965201	PH	ADB 965220	ED	ADB 965235	CF
ADB 965203	PB	ADB 965221	Preston	ADB 965236	CF
ADB 965204	IM	ADB 965222	BX	ADB 965237	IS
ADB 965205	Norwich	ADB 965223	IS	ADB 965238	LA
ADB 965206	DR	ADB 965224	TO	ADB 965239	LA
ADB 965207	IM	ADB 965225	Preston	ADB 965240	OC
ADB 965208	IS	ADB 965226	BX	ADB 965241	OC
ADB 965209	PB	ADB 965227	BX	ADB 965242	LE
ADB 965210	DR	ADB 965228	BX	ADB 965243	LE
ADB 965211	FW	ADB 965229	NH	ADB 965307	BS
ADB 965212	NH	ADB 965230	TO	ADB 965308	TI
ADB 965213	ED	ADB 965231	PH	ADB 965309	TI
ADB 965216	Carlisle				

Beilhack Type PB600 Plough on Class 40 Bogie

ADB 965576	Mossend Yard	ADB 965580	Carlisle	ADB 966097	EH
ADB 965577	Mossend Yard	ADB 965581	Carlisle	ADB 966098	Ashford
ADB 965578	SF	ADB 966096	EH	ADB 966099	Ashford
ADB 965579	SF				

Beilhack Self Propelled Rotary Snow Blower

ADB 968500	–	–	92 1980	IS
ADB 968501	–	–	100 1989	SL

Note: A separate worksplate on the detachable snowblower unit reads 119 1989.

Ashford Crane Repair Depot built four snowploughs in 1989. This photograph shows ADB 966099 at Ashford CRD on 28th July 1990.   Roy Hennefer

Wagon-mounted Snowblower 69001 is seen at Perth on 27th August 1990.   Roy Hennefer

CONTRACTOR'S, INDUSTRIAL AND OTHER NON-BR OWNED TRACK MACHINES

This additional section has been introduced for the first time in order that, as far as is currently possible, a complete record of the track machines that exist on British Railways (British Rail and non-British Rail) can be presented.

Whilst the details of those items owned by British Rail (and listed in the preceding chapters) include the whole range of powered on-track plant, this section deals specifically with track machines and track relayers. Therefore neither engineers trolleys/personnel vehicles nor cranes are included, although details of the former category can be found by consulting the Industrial Railway Society's current edition of 'Industrial Locomotives' (9EL).

In the next edition of this publication it is intended to further expand this section by also including those track machines owned and used by the preservation movement and in Ireland. Details of existing engineers trolleys owned by the preservation movement and in Ireland can be found by consulting 9EL (see above). As regards track machines on preserved railways, as the majority have CEPs numbers, details of those can be found by reference to the brief historys listed under 'Vehicles no longer in stock'.

For certain machines detailed in this section, mainly those acquired second-hand from Germany, precise builders number and date of construction are not yet available. It is anticipated that much of this information will however be available for the next edition, when it is hoped that a brief history of existing machines (when they have had more than one owner) can also be included. In addition some brief description details (when there is not an equivalent machine on British Rail) will also be given.

CONTRACTORS

The track machines owned by contractors can be found on railway sites all over the country, mainly on sidings owned by British Steel, British Coal, Ministry of Defence, Associated British Ports and the other major companies which are rail-connected. The main plant depot for each contractor is listed, although often machines are moved direct from one contract to the next. There is a concern amongst many British Rail civil engineering staff that the BRB will look to outside contractors, on an ever increasing scale, to carry out its traditional relaying and track maintenance operations.

BALFOUR BEATTY RAILWAY ENGINEERING
(PLANT DEPOT: RAYNESWAY, DERBY)

Manufacturer/Type	Builders Details
Plasser and Theurer UST 79S S&C Tamper	2606 1979
Plasser and Theurer 08–16/90 Split Head Tamper	2425 1989
Permaquip Mk V Ballast Packer	065 1986
Permaquip Mk V Ballast Packer	066 1987
Matisa R7D Ballast Regulator	–
Matisa R7D Ballast Regulator	–
Tamper Vibratool	
Set of Donelli Gantries	4371148
Set of Donelli Gantries	–

Road/Rail	Registration
Permaquip 3.5 tonne GVW	
Permaquip 3.5 tonne GVW	F 540 YCK
Newag Mercedes Unimog	F 615 FAO
Newag Mercedes Unimog	–
Lorry (Balfour Beatty conversion)	–
Wickham Crane Vehicle	KKL 253 P
	E 261 AHE

Notes:

1) As the amount of railway on-track plant owned by this company is growing rapidly, they intend to introduce a system of plant numbers during 1991.

2) Balfour Beatty Power will be taking delivery of three Road/Rail Newag Mercedes Unimogs during 1991.

GRANT LYON EAGRE
(PLANT DEPOT: SCOTTER ROAD, SCUNTHORPE)

Manufacturer/Type	Builders Details
Tamper Plain Line Electromatic EJG6 Tamper/Liner	376195 or 376205 c.1972
Tamper Plain Line Electromatic EJG6 Tamper/Liner	476245 c.1972
Tamper Switch Electromatic EJG6 Tamper/Liner	10810359 c.1981
Tamper Vibratool	–
Matisa R7D Regulator	6514 c.1975

HOFA ENGINEERING:
(PLANT DEPOT: BYASS WORKS, PORT TALBOT)

Manufacturer/Type	Builders Number
Tamper Vibratool	4371339
Road/Rail	Registration
Matisa Plain Line Tamper	FPP 404 T
Matisa Switch Tamper	A 241 UVV

TRACKWORK
(PLANT DEPOT: KAYTHORPE, GRANTHAM)

Manufacturer/Type	Builders Details
Permaquip Mk V Ballast Packer	067 1987

DINGLE BROS
(PLANT DEPOT: STEPPES HOUSE, BODMIN)

Road/Rail	Registration
DB30 Hedgetrimmer	C 301 FAF
DB30 Hedgetrimmer	C 302 FAF
774 Hedgetrimmer	E 575 RAF
DB30 Hedgetrimmer	E 576 RAF

GAMBLE
(PLANT DEPOT: MEADOW ROAD INDUSTRIAL ESTATE, WORTHING)

Road/Rail

Manufacturer/Type	Builders Number	Registration
Donelli KGT	4253	G 473 SUF
Donelli KGT	4261	H 867 YCD
Donelli KGT	4313	–

SHORTS
(PLANT DEPOT: BSC LLANWERN)

Road/Rail

Manfacturer/Type	Builders Number	Registration
Donelli KGT	4232	

HOPKINS
(PLANT DEPOT: MONASTRY LANE, SUTTON, ST HELENS)

Manfacturer/Type	Builders Number
Tamper Vibratool	4370765

HEDGEHOG SERVICES
(PLANT DEPOT: GRAVENEY HILL FARM, GRAVENEY, NEAR FAVERSHAM)
Road/Rail

Type	Registration
Hedgetrimmer	F 760 FKM
Hedgetrimmer	F 761 FKM
Hedgetrimmer	H 53 DKK

Note: During 1991, Hedgehog Services expect to also have available for use, a road/rail wood-chipper and a road/rail hedgecutter with a forty foot reach.

INDUSTRIAL
Most of the track maintenance carried out at industrial locations such as British Steel, British Coal, Ministry of Defence etc. is performed by contractors (see above) using their own on-track plant. However a number of sites still retain their own machines and these are detailed below.

Location	Manufacturer/Type	Builders Number
Ford, Dagenham	Matisa LCR04 Tamper	346
British Steel, Ebbw Vale	Matisa LCR04 Tamper	351
ICI Billingham	Matisa LCR04 Tamper	390

Geismar have built a ballast Hopper to work with a Scottish Plasser TASC-45. This picture shows it at the manufacturer's factory in Northampton.   Geismar

93

HIRE MACHINES

Several of the major suppliers to British Rail of on-track plant also hire out machines to British Rail and other customers.

GEISMAR

Type	Builders Details
Geismar MRT-2 Sleeper Changer	84012 153 1984
Geismar MRT-2 Sleeper Changer	88017 272 1988
Geismar PUMS (28)	82141–264 to 82141–271 inclusive
	82141–279/280
	85085–290 to 85085–297 inclusive
	87093–335 to 87093–340 inclusive
	88135–346/7
	88135–373/4

Road/Rail

Type	Builders Number	Registration
Donelli KGT	4206	–

Notes:

(1) The PUM Machines are designed for removal or installation of large parcels of track and S&C. They are extensively used throughout BR and on LUL. Each machine is accompanied by a matched trolley with swivelling platform and hydraulic scissor lift and slew facility.

(2) The KGT is the larger brother of the G.85 of which British Rail owns two. This machine, which was originally designed to a road/rail concept (rather than an adaption of a road machine), is extremely versatile and is capable of a wide range of excavating, lifting, grabbing, brush cutting duties etc. by easy changeover of tools. Another option is that the KGT and G.85 can be fitted with a 'man cradle' for overhead work, with operation of all controls from the cradle. None of the seven machines detailed in this book is currently fitted with that option.

PERMAQUIP

Road/Rail

Type	Registration
3.5 tonne GVW General Purpose Vehicle	F 511 LRR
11 tonne GVW (with crane)	G 276 NAU

Note: Both vehicles are fitted with Fairmont Hy-Rail equipment which transforms a standard commercial vehicle into a multi-purpose road/rail vehicle. Vehicles can be designed and manufactured to suit the needs of the customer and examples of the variants available can be found by consulting the section in this book on BR owned Road/Rail vehicles. At the time of writing the vehicles detailed above were on hire to the Eastern and Western Regions respectively.

TAMPER

Type	Builders Details
G04 Tracopher	4781268 1989

Note: This machine has been hired to both the Scottish and Southern Regions, whilst at the time of writing it is working in the North London area where it has been hired to both LUL and the London Midland Region. Whilst on BR it was temporarily numbered 76004, the three similar machines owned by BR being numbered 76001–3.

WICKHAM RAIL

Type	Builders Details
Type 44 Rail/Road Vehicle	801 1990

OTHER RAILWAYS

In addition to the industrial locations listed above, two railways have their own track machines as well as to any they might hire from time to time. It should again be emphasised that only track machines are listed here, as this information is not available elsewhere. As already stated 9EL should be consulted for details of the other powered departmental vehicles owned by both LUL and the Tyne and Wear Metro. For a comprehensive list of all types of LUL departmental stock the current edition of Capital Transport's 'London Underground Rolling Stock' is the definitive guide. It is also intended that Platform 5 Publishing Ltd. will produce a guide to all stock of LRT systems.

London Underground Ltd.

Manufacturer/Type	Running Number	Builders Details
Plasser and Theurer 07–16 Tamper/Liner	771	1753 1980
Plasser and Theurer 07–16 Tamper/Liner	772	1757 1980
Plasser and Theurer 07–16 Tamper/Liner	773	1758 1980

Tyne and Wear Metro

Manufacturer/Type	Builders Details
Tamper Switch Electromatic ES/TD Tamper/Liner	1076909 1979
Permaquip Platform Lift	017 1981
Plasser and Theurer 08–16M Tamper/Liner	2437 1989

PRINCIPAL MAINTENANCE DEPOTS

Area		Depot
Scottish North East	–	Perth
Scottish South East	–	Slateford
Glasgow	–	Shettleston and Rutherglen
Newcastle	–	Newcastle Forth Bank
Leeds	–	York Leeman Road
Doncaster	–	Doncaster Marshgate
Norwich	–	Norwich
Stratford	–	Stratford and Romford
Peterborough	–	Hitchin
Preston	–	Carnforth, Carlisle Upperby and Wigan (Springs Branch)
Manchester	–	Guide Bridge
Merseyside	–	Edge Hill
Crewe	–	Crewe Gresty Road and Chester
Nottingham	–	Nottingham (Eastcroft)
Birmingham	–	Wolverhampton (Wednesfield Road)
Watford	–	Rugby
Reading	–	Reading
Bristol	–	Bristol Marsh Jn. and Gloucester
Exeter	–	Taunton and Plymouth Tavistock Jn.
South Wales	–	Cardiff Cathays and Landore
Southern South East	–	Ashford and Hither Green
Southern Central	–	Three Bridges
Southern South West	–	Eastleigh and Woking

Most of the depots listed above are also responsible for the small plant allocated to their area. The exceptions are detailed below.

Newcastle	–	Darlington (Park Lane)
Leeds	–	Stanningley
Doncaster	–	Sheffield Woodburn
Preston	–	Lancaster Lune Road
Manchester	–	Newton Heath RCE Depot
Merseyside	–	Ditton
Crewe	–	Bangor and Crewe
Birmingham	–	Walsall
Watford	–	Watford and Northampton CMD
Bristol	–	Bristol Ashton Gate
Exeter	–	Exmouth Jn. and Plymouth (Valletort Road)
South Wales	–	Neath
Southern Central	–	Streatham Hill

The various main regional workshops are detailed below. The LMR and WR do not have a principle workshop for CCE plant maintenance.

Scottish Region	–	Kilmarnock
Eastern Region	–	York Leeman Road
Anglia Region	–	York Leeman Road
Southern Region	–	Ashford